HIBERNIAN NIGHTS

HIBERNIAN NIGHTS

By Seumas MacManus

INTRODUCED BY PADRAIC COLUM

Illustrated by Paul Kennedy

THE MACMILLAN COMPANY · NEW YORK

Ferguson, *St. Louis Post-Dispatch*

PREFACE

About Storytelling

BY SEUMAS MAC MANUS

STORYTELLING is the oldest and surely one of the loveliest of the arts, and when the world was younger, lustier and, in not a few ways, better, than today, it was necessarily one of the most prized, so largely did all the peoples depend on it for their nightly entertainment.

But today storytelling has become all but a lost art in almost every country. But my country, Ireland, cherished it most, brought it to greater perfection and held to it longest of all the western nations. The shanachie (storyteller) and the Bard, oft-times one, held the most honored place at court of every Prince and Chief, as well as in the hearts of the people. Long and hard years of learning for the noble profession they served in the Bardic schools, and rare were their rewards when at length they were vested with the cloak of the profession.

The art took a long, long time to wane with our people. In my childhood days, in my Donegal mountains, though the schooled professional shanachie had long disappeared, the homespun story-teller was plentiful—and cherished. There still was not a hill nor a glen but had its noted, sometimes famed and beloved practi-tioner who had inherited the great wealth of the ancient tales and spent the nights in lavish bestowment of his rare riches on the needy souls surrounding him. By a hundred happy hearths on a thousand golden nights, then I, with my fellows, enthroned me under the chimney brace, or in circle, hunkered on the floor in the fire glow, heartening to the recital, and spellbound by the magic of the loved tales so lovingly told by *fear-a'tighe* (man-of-the-house) or *bean-a-tighe* (woman-of-the-house). Not many women could be termed shanachie, but she was a poor mother who had not at least a dozen or twenty tales on which to bring up her children.

Thus and so, we Donegal children learnt the folk stories and the telling of them. Thus and so it was that we in turn propagated them. Thus and so it was that these fascinating tales through the long, long ages, gave to millions after millions, entertainment, happiness, joy, as well as the awakening and development in them of that beautiful imagination and sense of wonder that lightened, brightened and gilded lives that through near-hunger, hard labor and perpetual struggle with fate might well be expected to have been sore and sour to bitterness.

But the circumstances hard or otherwise, storytelling was ever a propagator of joy. The advent of printing and growth of reading it was that began the decline and finally the practical extinction of the hallowed art. Yet no multiplication of books and mushrooming of readers could compensate the world for the sad loss incurred. The read story never did, never will come near the benefiting quality of the told story. Two of the essential good qualities of the latter, the former never can capture. The read story may be said to be a dead story, prone on the printed page, entombed between boards, while the told story is a very much alive story, glowing, appealing and dancing with energetic vitality—the personality and inspiration that the good storyteller can always command into the tale he tells. While the read story may possess the value of the story alone, the told story carries, superimposed on it, the golden worth of a good storyteller's captivating art and enhancing personality—trebling its wealth.

CONTENTS

Also by SEUMAS MacMANUS

PLAYS

The Bachelor of Braggy (193–?)

The Miracle of Father Peter (193–?)

The Rale True Doctor (193–?)

Bong Tong Come to Balriddery (1906?)

The Hard-hearted Man (1906)

The Lad from Largymore (1906?)

Mrs. Connolly's Cashmere (1906?)

Nabby Harren's Matching (1906?)

Orange and Green (1906?)

Resurrection of Dinny O'Dowd (1906?)

Rory Wins: An After-Limerick Play (1906)

The Townland of Tamney (1906?)

Eleven One-act Plays (1905)

Woman of Seven Sorrows (1905)

AUTOBIOGRAPHY

The Rocky Road to Dublin (1938)

O, Do You Remember (1926)

HISTORY

The Story of the Irish Race (1921)

Ireland's Case (1919)

The Irish Position (1903)

CRITICISM

A Renaissance in Storytelling (1913)

INTRODUCTION

A STORYTELLER can bring to us all the emotions we can respond
to—delight, terror, suspense, recognition, gaiety. And there is
another emotion that seems primal in the storyteller's range—
wonder. In that great compendium of storytelling, the collection
we know as *The Arabian Nights* or *The Thousand and One
Nights*, the stories that trade in wonder are the ones that are most
memorable for us. And in the *Hibernian Nights* (remember that
Hibernian is the Latin for Irish) a wonder is always being told
to us.

The storyteller—I mean the person who actually recounts
stories—exists today. To be one of his audience you must seek
him in parts of the world where books are not readily available
and where the habit of reading is not ingrained. There are such
places in Ireland. There the storyteller—I will speak of "him"
although the teller will be a woman in some places—is named
shanachie.

The well-trained shanachie can hold his audience in different
locations and under different circumstances. On a platform in a
public hall in a city or among the surroundings of a drawing
room he can tell his stories with effect. But his inherited place is
by a fireside in a cottage where other cottages are few and far
between. There his surroundings are helpful to his narration.
Quietude is all around. The fire burns, not in a stove or a grate,
but on hearthstones level with the floor, a wide chimney above
it. There is a chair beside the fire, benches and stools around. The
fire is not of logs or coal: it is of peat or turf cut in the bog nearby, burning down into the ashes that are deep on the hearthstones. The walls are brown from the smoke of the peat; in the

ashes the crickets chirrup. And the cottage may be in such a solitude that the people listening to the storyteller can hear the curlews crying as they fly over it or the snipe in the bog nearby. There, seated on his chair with neighbors on benches or on stools around him, the shanachie can make very living or very humorous the happenings that are in his story.

He is respected as one who has a profession: he knows the history of the places, the genealogies of the people; he has acquired a repertoire of stories and he has been trained to tell them with remarkable openings, proper pauses for the lessening of tensions, notable climaxes. The man whose book we are reading told these stories before he wrote them down and collected them in *Hibernian Nights*.

Seumas MacManus was a shanachie by every title: he had listened to the shanachies in his native Donegal as he, a child, sat by a peat fire: he reverenced the old storytellers, going from one to another of them; he thought about the adventures of kings' sons and widows' sons as he herded sheep on the mountain or worked with other boys cutting peat. In his early manhood he was a teacher in a school that had thirty pupils, and at that stage he published stories and poems. In his published stories, not all of them traditional, there was such freshness of content, such unhackneyed method of narrative, that editors in the United States published them with the delight of discovery. What made him such a sought-after storyteller is indicated in a piece that has himself for a character.

After school on leaden November days Jamie was among the eloquent idlers—in the barn where the thresher was threshing, at the house where the thatcher was thatching, in the nailer's, the cooper's, the blacksmith's, the tinker's, the tailor's, the weaver's, or the shoemaker's. In gay bands he and his fellows deliciously roamed from one to another house of the busy ones, and found high entertainment in all. No biggest, gayest, busiest spot in the world offered to its idlers a vaster variety of pleasuring places than did Donegal, in its hundred hills and valleys. And surely none of all their high-priced pleasure palaces could offer such grand and continuous entertainment as was, night and day, in these houses presented free to all comers—with thanks and gratitude for the coming, thrown in. Only seldom again in his subsequent life, with its wide wanderings which brought him to gatherings of intellectual people and socially brilliant, did he get the high entertainment, mind-exaltment, soul-refreshment, which he absorbed from Stephen Williamson and his cronies in the mill-kiln; about John Burns's tailor-table or Briany MacDwyer's work-bench; in the joyful circle that hunkered on the earth-floor (for there was only one stool) around Shan O'Quigley the tinker, him at once narrating his adventures and plying his sothering iron.

From *The Rocky Road to Dublin*

Our shanachie came to the United States and made himself a figure on the platforms of colleges and literary societies. Part of the year he was back in Donegal.

To encounter Seumas MacManus on the lecture platform in America was to be made aware of how one who had learnt the art of storytelling by the peat fire in an Irish cottage could so skillfully transfer that long-descended art to other surroundings and other audiences. He brought the stories of a distant country and a distant past to places across mountains and prairies and deserts, and everywhere audiences responded to them. Once, he told me, he spoke in a town where his audience was a tribe of Sioux Indians. He kept them alert. And I have heard, in distant places, people speak of the stories they heard from Seumas MacManus years before. Remembering these audiences so far from where he had come, I think of the poem his admired friend, Alice Milligan, wrote about the poets who made their itinerary into places remote from their own country in the old days.

> At Carloway when you come
> (The way is wearisome)
> Men shall sit awed and dumb
> 'neath torch-lit rafter,
> But in that lonely Brugh
> When you are lost to view
> Then shall be talk of you
> For long years after.

> At winter in the hall
> When men sit silent all
> Watching the pine-logs fall
> To ash from ember,
> The King of Carloway
> Low murmuring your lay
> Shall murmuring smile and say
> "Do you remember?"

He named this collection, which includes fresh versions of stories from his many books, *Hibernian Nights*, with a deliberate glance toward the collection that has for its best-known title *The Arabian Nights*. Perhaps by the use of this title he wanted to show that his was a comprehensive collection. In many ways it is. Here are the main types of Irish storytelling—heroic quests, humorous exploits, shrewd judgments. We find ourselves in an ancestral world as we read *Hibernian Nights*. But here is no distant record of that world. The speech may be, as it often is, an evocation of wonder. But the wonder is related in the voice of a man entertaining his neighbors.

When Fergus reached the Castle of the King of the Eastern World, he began playing on his harp; whereupon all who heard—the servants, the guards, the soldiers, all—left every post and thronged out and around, listening in wonder and enchantment. When all were collected and their senses enspelled, Fergus scattered before them his bag of beech leaves, which now to their eyes looked like glistening gold pieces. They fell to scrambling and fighting for the riches —leaving Fergus to walk into the Castle and through door after door of twelve open doors, playing as he went—till he reached the innermost rooms—where the King, enchanted by the music, had fallen into a deep, deep sleep. Fergus entered and quick reached over the King's head for the Sword, giving a powerful pull. But the Sword, resisting, gave three bounds within its scabbard that shook the Castle to its foundation and let out three roars that were heard round half the world. In his sleep the King gave a great start—but didn't awake. Fergus set his teeth, grasped again the hilt, and pulled with all his might. The Sword then leapt and roared—the King bounded in bed, but fell back asleep. The teeth shook and rattled in Fergus' head— but gathering all his nerve and strength he gave a third mighty pull. The Castle rocked, the world was deafened, the King sprang awake from bed! But Fergus had the Sword from its sheath—waved it around his head and demanded to know who killed the Knight from Glendore.

There is invention in the telling of the stories, and although such invention is more spontaneous than deliberate, it should be noted—indeed, if it is not noted, half of their charm will be over-looked. The quality can be indicated in the opening of the story that follows the one we have quoted from.

There were, once on a time, a poor woman and her man named Nanny and Conn, who despite poverty, lived quiet and agreeable together, in peace, comfort, and content, though childless, for many years. One day Conn, coming from the potato field to get a bit of breakfast, found my brave Nanny sitting in the chimney corner sur-rounded by a bunch of neighbor women, all of them crying and whillelwing and pillelewing like the End of the World was coming up the road.

Here is a quality that is rare in modern writing—the quality of eloquence. It is the eloquence of a man speaking, who has fit words at his command, and who can place them in rhythmical utterance. To get the real effect one should give sound to the passage. Many readers will be chary of doing this because they will know it is—shall we say, Hibernian speech?—and therefore outside the ordinary reader's elocutionary habits. But if the reader makes no attempt to imitate any exotic speech he has heard, but reads the passage (or any passage) with the stress and pauses that are inherent in it, he will find that another charm has been given to the story, the charm of words and cadence, going to make an eloquence that is that of a man speaking to neighbors who themselves are eloquent.

The last time I saw our storyteller was at a memorial meeting for his friend, the American poet, Percy MacKaye. What was characteristic of the poet was brought before the gathering in a way that was characteristic of the storyteller. Seumas described Percy going into a Donegal cottage where, fascinated by the glow of turf fire, he wanted to sit in domestic semi-darkness. But, proud of the lamp he had paid three shillings and six pence for, his host was constantly calling on his daughter to light it so that his honored guest might have proper illumination. For half an hour, with humor and gentleness, Seumas MacManus made the scene live for us.

I thought of his first appearance—he had described it—before the great American editors fifty years before. He was a tow-headed, homespun-clad, pocket-bulging youth. He still seemed towheaded, for his thick crop was grizzled, not gray nor white. An unbent man, not rugged, but homespun, the glasses he wore gave him a kind of withdrawal; he had the slow speech of the Northerner—but maybe I should name it cadenced speech. As a youngster he had herded sheep on misty hills and cut turf in bogs. Through the book-knowledge he gave himself—and like all imaginative people for whom access to books is difficult, reading was a passion with him—he became a schoolmaster. In Donegal the pedagogue is not just a teacher: he is all that is implied in the word "schoolmaster"; he is always addressed as a "Master." For the young Seumas MacManus, the best of being a schoolmaster was in the hours spared from field and bog, when he could go far afield and gather lore at other than his neighbors' firesides. After having pieces published in the "locals" and some of the journals in the capital, he crossed the Atlantic as an envoy. The mission he was sent on was ludicrous. But another mission took its place, and this mission was real and acceptable. Seumas MacManus was to remain for many years Ireland's ambassador to America; this tall man with the cadenced voice, year after year, brought to audiences, North, South, East and West, the traditions of the Irish countryside. Memories, even the memories of those who were alienated by other Irish activities, were awakened by what he told on platforms and published in books, so that strands were reknit by him. Ireland, for thousands of people on this side of the Atlantic, was the Ireland of Seumas MacManus's bookwritings and storytellings. It remains an Ireland well worth hearing about, as readers of *Hibernian Nights* will find out for themselves.

PADRAIC COLUM

HIBERNIAN NIGHTS

THE SON OF STRENGTH

ONCE on a time when pigs were swine, the land of Donegal was in the habit of sending its men to Connacht to look for work and a living. Right bad masters the Connacht men made, burdening the Donegal men to break their hearts and backs and often end their lives. And the nearer it came to the ending of a Donegal man's term, the terribler were the tasks put to him, to force him to run away ere the wages fell due. And if they killed him outright, it only cost them the coffin.

One poor Donegal man harassed in this way was at length made by his master to shoulder an oak-tree, which broke both his back and heart and sent him home to die. So fierce was the grip he had held on the tree that an acorn on which his fist closed remained there, and no man could unclench his fist to release the acorn out till the day he died.

On the day that he came to die the man's wife bore him a son, and the dying man said, "My last request to you, Nabla, is that when I'm dead, you'll take the acorn from my fist and plant it;

and then nurse our son at your breast for seven years—and as much longer as till he is able to uproot the tree that comes of the acorn. The boy will be the Son of Strength, and you'll send him forth to punish the Connacht men for their cruelties and revenge their murdering of myself."

"I'll do that," said his wife.

And when he was dead, his wife forced his fist, took the acorn from it, and planted it.

She nursed the child at her breast till he was seven years old. By then the young tree was strong and stout, and she put the child to find if he could uproot it—but he failed. "I'll nurse you for another seven years," she said, "to see if you do better."

She nursed him at her breast for another seven years, and at end of that time, took her son again to test him on the oak—which was now tall and sturdy. But the lad failed again.

"I'll nurse you still another seven years," she said, "to try if you can best the tree then."

At the end of that time, the tree was great entirely, with roots reaching far and wide, and deep also—and she put her son to the test.

At the first pull the boy loosed the tree in the ground. At the second pull the roots ripped and tore. At the third he had the tree with him, and an acre of ground also, and with a shout and a whoop whirled the combination round his head like it was a sapling.

"That's good," said his mother. "You are now the Son of Strength, and can set out for Connacht to punish them who ruined your kin and killed your father."

Well and good. The boy trimmed the oak-tree for a walking stick, and getting his mother's blessing, set off for Connacht. When Connacht he made, the first man he met was the King himself, who asked him, "Who are you and what are you seeking?"

The lad answered, "I'm a boy looking for a master."

"That's good," said the King. "Myself's a master looking for a boy. What sample of work are you willing for?"

"Little partiality I have," said the Boy, "but I'm able to take a fall out of most anything comes my way."

"That's the order of boy myself is wanting," said the King.

"What's the wages and conditions?" asks the Boy.

"They're both simple and satisfying," says the King. "You're hired for a year and a day, and at the end I'll give you your weight in gold if you'll tackle and accomplish all work that's put before you. And if you fail, falter, or refuse any job, you'll be whipped at a cart-tail through three towns. Is that agreeable?"

"The wages are enticing," said the Boy, "and conditions agreeable to me. I'm your man," says he.

Very well and good. Next morning he was up betimes and asked the King on what work could he make an appetite for his breakfast.

"I'll soon show you that," said the King. And he led him out to the biggest barn the boy had ever beheld. It was a mile square and a hundred yards high. One half of it was piled with corn sheaves, and the other half cleared for thrashing. The King handed the boy a flail the size of himself, saying, "When you have that corn thrashed, stroll in for your breakfast. Not before." And he went off, chuckling.

The Boy looked first at the corn that half filled the big barn and then at the flail. In scorn he flung away the flail twenty miles, where it fell on a city and swept off all the roofs and the heads off half the inhabitants. Then he lifted his own walking stick and began thrashing the corn. Every whirl of his oak-tree knocked a bit out of the barn—and every whack whirled the straw to the skies. Showers of broken straw and whirlwinds of grain swept the land for fifty miles and terrified the population—who thought the end of the world was surely come.

Very soon he was finished, but two bits of the barn weren't left together. He went to the King to beg if there wasn't some other job which would pass the time till breakfast.

"Surely, you haven't all that corn thrashed?" said the King.

"Yes, and the barn into the bargain," said the Boy.

"That's a terrible thing—I'm ruinated!" said the King. Then he said, "I haven't anything more for you to do till you've gratified your appetite."

While he was breakfasting, the King consulted his advisers regarding this terrible fellow. And they all agreed that the man who could do what he did would likely kill all of them if they did not kill him first.

"But who'll kill him?" said the King.

Said they, "After his breakfast, send him to the Wood of the Wild Bulls to bring home a bull for dinner. No one ever ventured within seven mile of there and came back alive."

"That's a good idea," said the King.

After breakfast he told the Boy he needed a bull for dinner, and directed him to the Wood of the Wild Bulls to fetch one home.

"I'll do that," said the Boy.

Off he hied him and hadn't got within miles of the Wood till a covey of bulls came charging at him, with the King Bull at their head.

The Boy hailed them, "What's the hurry, lads? You'll all be dead long enough."

The King Bull, in a red rage and frothing at the mouth, was first to reach him. The Boy took hold of him by the two horns, swung him around his head, and with him beat the brains out of the nineteen bulls that traipsed after. Then he gathered in his grip the tails of the twenty, slung the bunch over his shoulder, and home with them, and flung the bunch down at the King's hall-door saying, "There's small good going all that journey to fetch you one bit of a bull. There's as many as will feed you for a fortnight. Is any other little job you need done?"

"No, no, no, no, no!" said the King, his teeth chattering. "No, no, thank you," said he "that's enough for one day. In the morning we'll see what's wanting next."

The King and his Counselors didn't sleep that night, but sat up discussing what they could do, at all, at all, to get rid of this dreadful fellow. They agreed that as he had destroyed the barn, he should be sent to the Dragon's Mountain to bring home timber for a new one. "The Dragon," they said, "will never let him escape alive."

Well and good. In the morning, when the Boy came wanting

his work, the King said he had nothing for him to do today, only cut and carry home from the Dragon's Mountain enough timber to build a new barn.

"I'll do that," said the Boy.

He went off, taking with him the biggest wagons and biggest horses about the castle. When he got on the Mountain, he tied a pair of horses to each oak-tree and began pulling them up by the roots. The Dragon, finding the hill shaking, came thundering down, with mouth like a mountain cave, to find what was doing. The first thing he met was two pairs of horses and their wagons —which he swallowed—carts, horses, and harness—without putting a tooth in them. And down his throat went the trees to which they were tied, also.

The Boy, turning, saw only the tails of the horses and the roots of the trees disappearing down the Dragon's throat. Said he, "After that breakfast, my bucko, you're fit for a fine day's work."

The Dragon, with his mouth wider still, was now coming for himself. The Boy pulled up the nearest oak-tree and at a spring landed straddle-legs on the Dragon's neck, and began whacking him with the tree, so that the brute reared like the Bull of Basham and went mad-running round the Mountain. The Boy laid on him with the oak-tree as hard as he could whack, and every clip he gave the Dragon, the laddo put out of him a yell like the end of the world! When soon he had the Dragon tamed, he ran a chain around a clump of fifty oak-trees, and fastening its other end to the animal's tail, mounted him again and headed him home.

With a howl, a yell, and a screech and a bound, the beast tore up by the roots the clump of oak-trees, and never stopped till the Boy halted him at the King's hall-door.

The King and his Counselors got under beds, up the chimneys, and down cellars. When the Boy would coax them to come forth, the King said he would do so only if the Boy drove the Dragon back to his Mountain again.

"Not hard is that," said the Boy. And loosing the load from him, he turned the Dragon's head for the hill, gave him a smack of the chains—and the beast streaked back to his Mountain like a streak of lightning.

"Is there any other little job I could do for you this morning?" asked the Boy.

"Thank you," said the King, "you've accomplished enough for the day. You may go now and enjoy yourself."

That night the King and his Counselors again sat up discussing what they should do to get rid of this terrible fellow.

They concluded that the one sure way to have his life was to send him next day to the Castle of the Giant of the Five Heads and Five Trunks, to demand from him seven horses, seven asses, seven cows, and seven mules, seven hens, ducks, geese, turkey-cocks, and pigeons, as tribute to the King of Connacht. The Giant would never let the Boy return alive.

In the morning then, the King told the Boy that all he asked from him this day was to take over to the Castle of the Giant of the Five Heads and Five Trunks, and get from him his tribute—seven horses, seven asses, seven cows, and seven mules, seven hens, ducks, geese, turkey-cocks, and pigeons.

"Is that all?" said the Boy. And he set off.

The King of Connacht ordered a great feast to celebrate their riddance of the fellow, now and forever. But lo! in the feast's middle, a breathless messenger burst in to tell them jump quick to the windows and see what they'd see.

With the uneaten bits in their mouths choking them, the King and his Counselors leapt to the windows, and the sight they saw coming over the hill was the Boy, bent double under the Giant's big barn chained on his back, and filled with horses, asses, cows, and mules, their heads through the windows, mooing, neighing, and braying, routing and roaring like the end of the world! while hens, ducks, geese, turkey-cocks, and pigeons were ranged on the rigging, cackling and quacking, and cooing and crowing to deafen the dead! The Giant, himself, was strapped to the back of the barn with his five heads roaring all at the same time. And between himself, his fowls, and his animals, the riot they made was ridiculous.

The King and his Counselors fought like soldiers for the best hiding-place. And when the Boy dumped the menagerie at the hall-door, the King couldn't be coaxed from under the best bed till the Boy had to shoulder his load, and haul it away again, complaining that he couldn't be bothered with this sort of unsatisfactory employment.

After another night's consultation between himself and his Counselors, the King next morning told the Boy that his chore for that day was to go to Hell and bring from there the King's grandfather, who was wanted as witness in a border dispute between the Kings of Connacht and Leinster.

"And how am I to know your grandfather?" asked the Boy.

"You'll know him," said the King, "by his wearing a red skull-cap and drinking his soup with a noise."

"Very well," said the Boy. And he set off.

"Now, thanks be to Heaven," said the King, "we are rid of the vagabond, anyway." And all the King's Counselors thanked Heaven from their hearts, too. But behold you! two hours weren't gone, when breathless servants called on the King and the Court to rush to the windows and see what they'd now see. They rushed to the windows, and the sight they beheld was half of Hell in red skull-caps galloping down the hill, and the Boy lashing them before him with a fiery flail.

"What's this? What's this? What's this, in the name of both Heaven and Hell?" cried the King when the clanjaffry charged onto the castle lawn.

Said the Boy, "I found half of Hell wearing red skull-caps and drinking their soup with a noise, so I found the handiest thing was to fetch them all here, and let you pick your grandfather out of the pack."

"Take them away, for Heaven's sake!" begged the King. "If you'll only take them away, I'll never interrupt my gratitude to you till the day I die!"

Said the Boy, "I'm soon going to get vexed with this sort of employment. You're the hardest-to-please master ever I hired to, and I'm going to be sorry before I've put in my time with you."

He wheeled the regiment around, however, and with a crack of the flail sent them scurrying home to Hell again. "Is there any other little thing you need done today?" said he.

"Thank you," said the King, "that's enough for this day. You may go and enjoy yourself."

That night the King and his Counselors, to their great delight, hit upon a plan that would most certainly rid them of the Boy for good and all. And they wondered why they hadn't thought of it at first. Below the castle, a well was being dug and was now three hundred feet down, and in the morn they'd order the Boy to continue the digging whilst they'd crush and bury him when they got him below. Three great granite millstones would be trundled to the hole by a batch of men, and thrown down on him. And then a hundred more men would start flinging clay on top of the corpse.

Bright and early the next morning, the Boy was with the King, asking for something to do. And the King said that all he would need him to bother about today would be to go in the new well without and lower it another hundred feet.

"I'll do that," said the Boy.

Down the well he went, and soon as he had disappeared, three great millstones were trundled to the hole and thrown down on him, and a hundred men fell to shoveling tons of clay down after. The King and his Counselors were watching the fun from the castle windows—and great was their glee that now the Boy was finally done for.

But behold you! when the shovelers had been shoveling half an hour, up pops the Boy's head with one millstone on it like a hat—the crown of the head just showing through the center hub-hole—and the other two millstones on his wrists like bracelets!

Out he bounded, shaking himself like a dog coming out of a river—shaking ten tons of clay off him, and scattering it for half a mile on every side. Forward to the castle he stepped, in hat and bracelets, and upspoke to the King, who was too thunderstruck to run away from the window.

"I want to warn you," he said, "that I refuse to do one other stroke of work in that hole unless you station a young lad at the mouth to shush the crows away from scraping dirt down atop of me. Ugh! my mouth and eyes are full of it. Here's a hat," said he, "that some good Christian, who knew what I needed, threw down to me, and two other new ones I'm carrying on my wrists to save for Sundays. Would you mind putting the two away carefully for me? The one on me head I need to keep the sun off."

The King fainted, and nothing brought him to till they'd emptied a barrel of brandy over him.

When he was to himself he said to the Boy, "Considering that you're such a good Boy, and have done more work in a week than I hired you to do in a year, you have well earned your wages. I'll weigh them out to you and let you go to your home for which, I know, your heart's hungering."

"You're too kind," said the Boy.

"Don't mention it," said the King. "Take off your hat and get on the scales."

"Take off my hat!" said the Boy. "You'll next ask me to take off my shirt and shoes. You didn't put that in the bargain when you hired me. You'll weigh me, if you please, with all my clothes on."

Into the scales he stepped, then, and I assure you that little gold was left in the King's cellar, when they'd weighed himself and the hat!

And when he got the gold on his back to start for home, he said, "Good-bye to you, King, and since I find you such a prompt pay-master, I'll be back again to hire for another term as soon as I've left this money with my mother."

"No, no! no! no!" cried the King. "With all that gold to your name, you're far too respectable to be anybody's servant-boy. If you promise never to come back, I'll promise that neither my-self nor any other man in Connacht will ever again mistreat any man in future who comes here to hire from Donegal."

Said the Boy, "Then, it's a bargain."

Home to Donegal went the Boy, bent under his golden burden. His poor father's murder was avenged, and the Connacht men cured. A castle he built, with a window for every day in the year. He made in it, for his mother, a throne of gold, and married a King's daughter, and lived happy and well ever after.

THE TINKER OF
TAMLACHT

LONG, long ago there lived in Donegal, in a place called Tamlacht, a poor tinker who was known as the Tinker of Tamlacht. A mighty poor man was he.

There was a morning he got up out of his bed and there was nothing in the house to eat, for himself and his wife. The meal-chest was empty and so was the cupboard. No more was there any money in his pocket.

But as good luck would have it, a call came for him that morning to go six miles over the mountains to fix a still. He went there, and he fixed the still and got paid—three silver shillings, which he put in his pocket—and started for home along the mountain road.

He followed the mountain road till it struck a bog—and went circling around the bog; but the Tinker, a-hurry to get home to where his wife was hungering for her breakfast, left the high road and took a near-cut across the bog.

Now when the Tinker ran into the bog, he found himself

sinking and sinking and sinking at each step, and he got so provoked at length that he stopped in middle of the bog and said from his heart,

"May the Devil take me if ever I come this way again!"

Well and good. The Tinker, at length, got out of the bog and onto the high road again, following it till he came to a crossroads. There he saw a miserable, wretched, ragged beggar crouched, who put out a skinny hand and asked for alms for God's sake.

Now the Tinker of Tamlacht, tenderest-hearted man in all Ireland, never turned a deaf ear to the cry of distress, never could deny anything to anybody, put his hand in his pocket, took out a silver shilling, and gave it to the beggar—got a "God bless you" —and went on.

A mile farther on he came to another crossroads, and there was another miserable, wretched, ragged beggar crouched, who put out a skinny hand and asked for alms for God's sake. The Tinker of Tamlacht, tenderest-hearted man in all Ireland, never turned a deaf ear to the cry of distress—he put his hand in his pocket, took out a silver shilling and gave it to this creature, got a "God bless you!" and went on.

Within a mile of his own home he came to a third crossroads and there saw a third miserable, wretched, ragged beggar, who put out a skinny hand and asked for alms for God's sake. The Tinker of Tamlacht, tenderest-hearted man in all Ireland, came to a standstill! He put his hand in his pocket, took out his third and last shilling, looked at it in his hand, looked from it to the hungry beggar, and thought of his wife who was hungering for her breakfast at home—and his heart was torn. He said to the beggar, "I have only one silver shilling left between myself, my wife, and starvation. I'll tell you what I'll do—I'll break this shilling and give you half of it."

"No," said the beggar. "Give me all or give me nothing!"

The Tinker of Tamlacht, tenderest-hearted man in all Ireland, who never turned a deaf ear to the cry of distress, reached his last shilling to the beggar!

The instant he did so, the miserable, wretched, ragged figure rose up, the rags fell from it, and lo and behold! it was a shining

Angel was standing in the road before the Tinker! The Angel said, "I have tested you three times this morning, and find you're a man after God's own heart. Now you must be rewarded. I give you any three wishes in the world."

The Tinker, delighted, said, "I know what my first wish will be."

"What is it?" said the Angel.

"It is," said the Tinker, "that my meal-chest, which is empty at home, may be filled with meal."

The Angel smiled and said, "You have your wish. What's your second wish?"

The Tinker had to think a long time to know what, when his meal-chest was filled, his second wish could be. But at length he remembered. He said, "Yes, I have a second wish," he said. "When I go to a mountain house to fix a pot or a pan or a still, and lay down on the floor this budget of tools that I am carrying on my shoulder, every little child will come to it, and one of them will carry away one tool, another will take another tool, and so on, till, when I go to the budget to look for a tool, it isn't there. Now," he said, "I wish that anything goes into that budget may never be able to get out again till I let it out."

The Angel smiled and said, "You have your wish. What is your third wish?"

The Tinker took a long time to know what other wish he could possibly have in this world, but at length he remembered, and he said,

"Yes, I have a third wish. By my little cabin at home," he said, "I have a little garden, and in that garden there's one apple tree. That apple tree has borne apples for thirty years, but I never knew the taste of one of my own apples yet. Because," says he, "every little vagabond going to and coming from school, breaks into my garden and steals all the apples before they're half-ripe. Now," he said, "I wish that anyone who ever puts a hand to one of them apples, that his hand may stick to the apple, and the apple stick to the tree, until I release them."

The Angel smiled and said, "You have your wish. And I only wish that you had wished for greater things"—and disappeared.

But the Tinker considered he had got the greatest things in the world and went home happy.

He was happier still, when he came home, to find his meal-chest filled and overflowing. He and his wife lived happily on that meal-chest for two months. At the end of that time, the meal-chest was eaten down and empty.

Next morning when the Tinker got out of his bed he was heavy-hearted. There was nothing to eat in the house. But as good luck would have it, there came a call for him, that morning again, to go to the same place over the mountains to fix a still. He went there, fixed the still, got paid, and started home along the mountain road. He followed the mountain road till it reached the bog and went circling around it. But the Tinker, in a hurry home, left the high road and again took the near-cut across the bog.

But lo and behold you! he hadn't rightly got in the bog until he found himself tapped on the shoulder; and, looking around, whom should he see at his elbow but the Devil!

The Tinker was dumfounded! When his speeches came to him he said to the Devil, "To what do I owe the honor of this visit?"

The Devil said, "You must have a mighty short memory. Two months ago you were crossing this bog before, and you stopped in the bog's middle and said from your heart, 'May the Devil take me if I ever come this way again!' Now here I am to carry out my part of the contract."

The poor Tinker had to bow his head and go with the Devil.

Out of the bog the Devil took him, along the high road, on the way to his own Place. Now the high road to Hell happened to lead past the Tinker's own village, and when they came nigh to the village, the Tinker stopped on the road and said to the Devil,

"I've no doubt but you're both decent and respectable in your own way, but the people in my village have a prejudice against you."

"Well," said the Devil, "how can I help it?"

"You can help it," the Tinker said. "Everyone knows you have the power of changing yourself into any shape you like. All you have to do is change yourself into some shape so no one will

know you while we're going through my village where everyone knows me. When we come to the other side of the village
where nobody knows me, come back to your own shape again."

"All right," said the Devil, who likes to oblige his friends,
"What change shall I make?"

"The handiest change you can make," said the Tinker, "is to
turn yourself into a bit of lead and go into my budget here."

The poor, innocent Devil, little suspecting, turned himself into
a bit of lead and went into the Tinker's budget. The Tinker
snapped the budget to, hoisted it on his shoulder, and away with
him to the nearest blacksmith's forge. There he threw down the
budget on the anvil, and to half a dozen, big, lusty farmer's sons
standing round, he said, "Boys, as I came along, I found something leaping and jumping in this budget. I don't think it's good.
Take a hold of them sledges and test what's in it."

The big fellows, every one of them, got hold of a sledge. The
first lad swung the sledge around his head and with all the
strength of his arm, came down on the budget on the anvil—
drawing a screech out of the budget! And when the next lad,
and the next, and next came down on the budget, there was a
howl and a yell and a scream and a screech, and, "Let me out!
Let me out! LET ME OUT!"

"By the powers, boys," the Tinker said, "I do believe it must
be the Devil, himself, is in the budget! Now the time may come,
boys, when he may have the upper hand of you, but now that
you have the upper hand of him, take it out of him!"

When the lads heard 'twas the Devil in the budget, it's little
encouragement they needed. Every one of them swung his sledge
around his head and with all the power of his arm and venom of
his heart brought down his sledge on the budget on the anvil;
and every stroke that came down fetched a howl and a yell and
a scream and a screetch out of the budget, and, "Let me out! *Let
me out!! LET ME OUT!*"

But the Tinker wouldn't let him out, and when at length the
life and soul were beaten out of the poor Devil in the budget, up
he rose, budget and all, carrying off the roof in a flame of fire,
and disappeared.

The Tinker, free, went home happy. And he was happier still, when he got home, to find that his wife had presented him with a baby. She asked him to go out and get a godfather for their baby.

The Tinker went out to find a godfather. And the first man he met was the big, rich, English landlord of that place, who asked him where he was going. The Tinker said, "I'm looking for a godfather for my baby." The big *bodach* of a landlord said, "Will you take me?"

"No," the Tinker said, "I'll not take you. You've smiles for the rich and frowns for the poor. You'll not be the godfather of my baby."

And he went on.

The next he met upon the road was God, who, when he learnt the Tinker's mission, asked him, "Will you take Me?"

"No," the Tinker said. "I'll not take You. You let that big rich *bodach* [scoundrel] of a landlord on the hill there above get richer every day, and this poor widow with seven children down the valley, you let get poorer. I'll not have You as godfather for my baby."

And he went on.

Next he met upon the road was Death, and Death asked him where he was going. He said, "I'm looking for a godfather for my baby." And Death said, "Will you take me?"

"Yes," the Tinker said. "I'll take you. You're the fairest and justest in all the world. To you, high and low, rich and poor, young and old, are all alike. You will be godfather for my baby."

He took Death home, and Death stood godfather.

"And now," Death said, "you must be rewarded for choosing me as godfather."

Out from his belt he took a small bottle and handed it to the Tinker. He said, "Here is a bottle that can never be emptied, no matter how much you pour out of it. It's a bottle of *Ioc Slainte* [Ointment of Health]. Three drops of it on the tongue of any sick person who is curable, and no matter how ill he is, he'll be instantly cured. I give you this bottle, and I also give you the power of seeing me. When you enter a sickroom, you'll see me

standing either at the head or the foot of the bed. If I am standing at the head of the bed, *I have marked that person for myself.* Your bottle is of no use there. But *if you see me standing at the foot of the bed*, then no matter how sick the invalid is, three drops from your bottle on his tongue and he'll be instantly cured." And Death, after giving him the bottle, disappeared.

The Tinker went out to test his bottle, and hearing there was a girl dying (as they thought) in a certain cottage, he went there, went into the sickroom. And saw Death standing at the foot of the bed. Then pouring three drops of *Ioc Slainte* from his bottle onto the girl's tongue, the girl, who was dying (as they thought) sat up in bed, talking and chatting and laughing, completely cured!

The amazed people in the sickroom ran out over the country, telling of the Tinker of Tamlacht and his wonderful bottle. And now, wherever there was anyone ill they were sending for the Tinker. And to everyone's amazement, the moment the Tinker entered a sickroom, he could tell whether the sick one was curable or incurable—and if he was curable, he would cure him instantly with three drops from the bottle on his tongue.

His fame spread fast, and from far and near, north, south, east, west, they were sending for the Tinker of Tamlacht. And for a hundred years he went up and down Ireland, curing all who were curable—gathering gold and gathering gear, lands and strands, cattle and castles—all were his. And at the end of a hundred years he was the wealthiest as well as most famed man in all Ireland.

One day, after a hundred years, he was driving along a mountain road in Donegal—driving in his coach-and-four, he, who used to tramp these roads, a ragged, poor tinker, with budget on his shoulder! Passing by a little cabin he heard a heart-rending wail come from it.

Now the Tinker of Tamlacht, tenderest-hearted man in all Ireland, could never turn a deaf ear to the cry of distress. He made his coachman halt, got out of the coach and went into the

Death said, "Here is a bottle that can never be emptied, no matter how much you pour out of it."

little cabin—where he found a poor widow wailing and weeping heartbreakingly, because, she said, her son and sole support was dying in the room.

He said to her, "Let me see him. I'm the Tinker of Tamlacht."

When she heard it was the famed Tinker of Tamlacht, she was overcome with joy. She cried, "Come with me! Come with me and cure my son!"—leading the Tinker to the room.

But lo and behold! When he entered the sickroom the Tinker saw *Death standing at the head of the bed!* He shook his head sadly and said, "My poor woman, I'm sorry for you. I cannot cure your son"—and went out.

The poor woman followed and threw herself on her knees on the road before him, imploring him, for Heaven's sake, and for all sakes, to return and cure her son. "For, if he dies," she said, "I'll die, too, of a broken heart."

The Tinker of Tamlacht, tenderest-hearted man in all Ireland, never turned a deaf ear to the cry of distress, paused on the road and took thought. He said to the poor woman,

"Will you get me four fine, big, strong young men?"

She got him four fine, big, strong young men, and he said to them,

"Come with me." And led them into the cabin and up to the sickroom, where he planted the four fine, big, strong, young men, one man at each corner of the bed. And when he had planted the four fine, big, strong young men, one at each corner of the bed, he clapped his hands for signal and said,

"Quick, boys! Turn the bed right around!"

And the boys, quick, turned the bed right around, leaving Death now standing at its foot. The Tinker went and poured three drops of *Ioc Slainte* from his bottle on the tongue of the dying boy, and the dying one sat up in bed, talking and chatting and laughing—completely cured! Better than ever he had been in all his born days!

The Tinker of Tamlacht had got many a golden fee at many a castle in the land, but he thought he had never left any castle, with a golden guinea in his pocket, one half as happy as he left that little cabin that day, covered with the gratitude and the blessings of that poor widow.

Happily, he would step into his coach again—but as he would, he found himself tapped upon the shoulder, and turning around, there was Death, standing by his elbow! Death said, "You thought to trick me, but they that laugh last, laugh best. Now your own career is ended. Come with me!"

And the Tinker of Tamlacht had to bow his head and go with Death—who took him away, along the road, making his way to the Next World.

It happened that on the way they had to pass by the little cabin in which the Tinker used to live, a hundred years ago, when he was only a poor tinker.

The Tinker called Death's attention to the cabin and said,

"It's many a happy day I've passed in that little cabin, more than a hundred years ago when I was only a poor tinker; and when I'm in the Next World, it's often and often I'll think of my happy days there. Would you let me have a little memento from it, to take into the Next World with me?"

"Surely," says Death. "What would you like to have?"

"Would you mind," said the Tinker, "going into the garden and plucking one of the apples off of that apple tree?"

"It's a mighty small request," says Death. "I'll pluck you a dozen."

"Oh, one will do," said the Tinker.

Into the garden went Death and started to pluck an apple from the tree, but lo and behold! when he took hold of the apple, his hand stuck to the apple and the apple stuck to the tree! He pulled and he tugged, but couldn't get away. And he called to the Tinker, "Come here and pull me away!"

"Oh," said the Tinker, "you've been a long time walking the world. Just take a rest to yourself now."

And leaving Death sticking to the apple tree, the Tinker started over the world, now curing all before him. His name and fame had now gone to the ends of the earth, and from the earth's ends, high and low, rich and poor, noble and knight, beggar and baron—everyone who was ill was sending for the Tinker of Tamlacht. And all were being cured.

For a hundred years now he went up and down the world, curing all who were ill—and for a hundred years nobody in all the world died. And the Tinker was gathering more gold and gear, lands and strands, cattle and castles—till he became the wealthiest and most famed man in the whole world.

At the end of a hundred years, he happened to be driving over the same mountain road in Donegal again, and, passing by his little cabin, he glanced from his coach and saw Death still sticking to the apple tree. And he said, "Is it there you are yet?"

"Oh," Death implored, "I have suffered sufferings untellable in the hundred years I've been hanging here. Let me free! Let me free! Let me free, and I'll give you another hundred years to live!"

The Tinker of Tamlacht, tenderest-hearted man in all Ireland, never turned a deaf ear to the cry of distress. He said, "All right. Let go!" And Death let go.

And if Death had been getting nobody for the last hundred years, now he started over the world reaping a rich harvest, trying to make up for all he had lost in the hundred years that were gone.

But the Tinker of Tamlacht didn't mind, for he had gathered all the gold and all the gear that the heart of man could wish. And for another hundred years he was living on the ridge of the world, enjoying all the world's joys—for a hundred years that passed like a single year, so joyous were they.

There was a night at last, that, in his castle, after his supper, he was sitting enjoying this pipe and his bottle, when he found himself tapped upon the shoulder, and turning around, there he saw Death standing, grinning down at him. Death said, "Now, your hundred years are up. Now, you come with me."

The poor Tinker was dumfounded. But when he got his speeches, he said, "Well, if I must go with you, I must. But do you know," he said, "I have so many and such great possessions that I need time to leave my affairs in order. Wait till I make my will."

"I have no time to wait!" cried Death. "Come!"

The Tinker pleaded, and pointing to a candle on the table that was burnt to within an inch of its socket, he said, "I only want you to wait till that candle burns out!"

"All right," snapped Death. "Get at it. I'll not take you till the candle's burnt out."

"That's good," said the Tinker, blowing out the candle. "The candle will never burn out."

Death flew into a rage, and he danced around the Tinker, vowing vengeance. But nothing could he do, for he had given his promise not to take the Tinker until the candle had burned out.

The Tinker of Tamlacht carefully took the bit of candle to a bog and buried it a hundred feet deep, to insure that it would never burn again.

But Death, all vengeful, kept the buried candle in mind till, in a hundred years, the bog wore down to it. And then he got and burned it out.

During that hundred years the Tinker of Tamlacht had been living on the ridge of the world, enjoying all the world's joys— a hundred years that had passed like a single year, so joyous were they.

On a night at the end of that time, the Tinker, in his castle, after his supper, sitting with his pipe and his bottle, found himself tapped upon the shoulder, and turning around, beheld Death grinning down at him. Death told him that the candle had burned out.

"And now," Death said, "you come with me!"

The Tinker was dumfounded, but when his speeches came to him, he said, "Well, if I must go with you, I must. But do you know," he said, "I am mortally ashamed of going into the Next World with the story on my lips that in the past three hundred years I haven't put up a single prayer to God. I want you to wait while I say some prayers."

Death cried, "I have no time to wait! Come! Come!"

"Oh," the Tinker pleaded, "I only want you to wait till I put up one pater-and-ave!"

"All right," snapped Death. "Be quick about it! I'll not take you till you've said a pater-and-ave."

"That's good," said the Tinker. "I'll never more say a pater-and-ave in my life."

Death flew in fearful rage and danced around the Tinker, vowing vengeance, but the Tinker laughed at him right heartily. For nothing could Death do to him since he had given his word not to take him till he'd said a pater-and-ave.

For another hundred years the Tinker lived on the ridge of the world, enjoying all the world's joys—for a hundred years that once again passed like a single year, so joyous were they.

And on a night after a hundred years, the Tinker was driving in his coach-and-four over a mountain road in Donegal; and passing over a bridge, he heard a wild wailing come from under the bridge. The Tinker of Tamlacht, tenderest-hearted man in all Ireland, never turned a deaf ear to the cry of distress. He halted his coach, got out and went down under the bridge, where he saw a wretched, piteous, poor object huddled, wailing and wailing heartbreakingly.

The Tinker's heart was touched. He said, "My poor creature, who are you and what's the matter with you?"

The object looking up at him said,

"I——am——a——soul! I'm a soul who lived in the world seven hundred years ago, and for seven hundred years have been suffering in purgatory because of a penance laid on me on earth, which I neglected to say. And from purgatory I can never be released till I find some mortal who will say my penance for me."

"My poor creature," the tinker said, "if it's anything a poor sinner like me can say for you, you'll soon be released. What is it?"

Said the miserable object, "When I was in the world, seven hundred years ago, there was a penance laid on me to say one pater-and-ave, which I neglected to say. If you say that for me, I'll be instantly released."

"In troth, then, my poor creature," the Tinker said, "you'll soon be released."

On his knees flopped the Tinker and put up a pater-and-ave.

And the instant he was finished, the miserable object rose up, the rags fell from it, and lo and behold you! there stood Death!

Death grinned down at the Tinker and said, "Now, you've said your pater-and-ave. Now you come with me. Now you trick me no more!"

The Tinker, when he came from his dumfounding, bowed his head and said, "I'm ready to go with you. In the hundreds of years I've lived on earth, I've enjoyed all the joys that man can know in this world. I'm ready to go and try the joys of the next."

And he went with Death, who took him to the Next World, up and up and up, till they came to Heaven. Death knocked on the gates, and Saint Peter came and asked, "Whom have you with you?"

And when Death answered, "The Tinker of Tamlacht," Saint Peter thundered,

"The *Tinker of Tamlacht!* Is it the fellow who wouldn't have God as godfather for his baby? Take him away! Take him away! Take him away! Take him away from here!"

"You see," said Death, "your character is up here before you. I'm sorry. There's nothing now, but try down the other place."

Down the road the two of them went trotting till they came to Hell. When Death knocked on the gates, a great voice from within bellowed: "Who have you there now?"

When Death answered, "The Tinker of Tamlacht," a fearful roar came out of Hell: "THE TINKER OF TAMLACHT!—I had one experience of that fellow! Take him away! Take him away! Take him away from here! If I let that fellow in here, he'd make this place too hot for us! Take him away! Take him away from here!"

"You see," said Death, "Your character's down here before you, too. They'll admit you neither Above nor Below. What am I to do with you? I must put you back on earth again."

Said the Tinker, "When I was on earth, I enjoyed all the joys that man on earth can know. I'll not consent to go back on earth unless you contrive to put me there in some new shape."

Said Death, "I can't have you on my hands, going round the

world and round the world for the remainder of the days of the world. Anything to get rid of you! In what shape would you like to go back?"

Said the Tinker, "When I was a boy, young and innocent, living on the banks of the River Erne in Donegal, there was many and many a lovely summer day I sat on the green banks of the Erne, watching the salmon leaping and playing in the river and leaping the Falls. I used to think there was nothing in all the world happier than those salmon. I want you to make me a salmon in the River Erne."

And Death made him a salmon in the River Erne.

That was five hundred years ago. The Erne is the best salmon river in all Ireland, and great sportsmen come from many countries to fish for salmon there. And during the ages since, all fishermen who come are sorely provoked by one notorious salmon with a brown spot on its shoulder, who, when they are fishing, is always leaping and playing out in front, tempting and taunting and sorely provoking every man of them. And the greatest and keenest fishers come back revengefully year after year, vowing that they'll catch that taunting, tempting, provoking fellow, and end his antics. But no one of them has ever been able to catch that salmon, and no one of them ever will catch that salmon. For that salmon is the Tinker of Tamlacht, leaping and playing himself in the River Erne, where he will leap and play to the end of the world's days.

THE

THREE GOLDEN EGGS

ONCE upon a time, long, and long, and very long ago, there were a King and a Queen of Connacht who had one daughter, Maeve. And a beautiful girl she was, the loveliest in all Ireland, and as good as she was lovely.

Now the Queen died, and the King married again, a woman who had one daughter, called Sorcha. An ugly girl Sorcha was, and as unlikable as she was ugly. The new Queen right heartily disliked Maeve because she was so much more beautiful and so much more beloved than her own daughter.

At this time it happened that the King of Greece died, and the young Prince, his son, who was to succeed him, went traveling over Europe, searching for a fitting and beautiful girl to be his wife and Queen of Greece. He had now reached Ireland and was riding around it on his search.

When the Queen, Maeve's stepmother, heard that he was nearing Connacht, she called in the dressmakers and the beautifiers, and had her daughter, Sorcha, trimmed and a-trigged and dressed and beautified in the grandest fashion, feeling sure that the Prince would choose her to be his Queen.

To get Maeve out of her daughter's way and place her beyond all chance of choice, she put her in a ragged dress, tied an old handkerchief on her head, and sent her out to herd the geese.

When the Prince was riding up to the King's castle, he, through a hedge, got a glimpse of Maeve herding geese in a field and was instantly smitten with love of her. And when he came into the castle and met the Queen, he told her how he had just glimpsed the loveliest goose-girl ever he had seen in all his life, and would like to see more of her.

"Not at all," says the Queen, says she. "That girl is far from beautiful, and besides, is a beggar-woman's daughter who would disgrace you. But," says she, "I have here my own daughter, the most beautiful of all Ireland's girls. You will fall in love with her the instant you see her, and she will make a proud Queen of Greece."

But when Sorcha was brought in, and the Prince saw her, he was disgusted. "I will go out," says he, "and seek that goose-girl."

He found Maeve, spoke with her and fell more deeply in love with her. He said to his attendants, "I don't care if she is a goose-girl and a beggar-woman's daughter, I'll make her the Queen of Greece!"

But as he would propose to her, twenty soldiers sent out by the Queen seized Maeve and whisked her away—and off to the castle before he knew what he was about. Then the Prince took consultation with the Commander and attendants who rode with him; and it was agreed that they would steal into the castle that night and carry off Maeve. From a herd boy he learned that she was a real princess, and he hired this herd boy, who knew where Maeve slept, to direct them to her chamber in the night.

But the herd boy gossiped to the servants at the castle, and they alarmed their mistress, the Queen, of the Prince's plot. And lo and behold! didn't she that night put her own ugly daughter, Sorcha, to sleep in Maeve's bedchamber and put Maeve to sleep in Sorcha's bed. So, when the Prince and his company, directed by the herd boy, stole into the castle at midnight, it was the sleeping Sorcha that they wrapped up in her bedclothes and carried off with them; and the Prince had Sorcha before him on his horse as he galloped away.

All night they galloped, till, in the morning, when they felt they were safe from pursuit, they halted at another castle—and this was the Queen's own sister's. They asked for and got hospitality here, and when they unwrapped the girl—behold you!—the Prince to his disgust discovered that it was the ugly Sorcha he had, instead of beautiful Maeve! He told her aunt to send her home again, and said he would return and never come back without the maiden who had won his heart.

At this, Sorcha's aunt flew into a rage. Bad as was her sister, the Queen, this was a worse woman still, and a witch besides. And as the young Prince rode out of the castle gates, she cast on him her spells and changed him into a hawk!

But if she changed his form, she couldn't change his heart. The Hawk so loved the beautiful Maeve that it flew to the King of Ireland's castle and lit in the trees beside it; and when Maeve came to walk in the garden, the Hawk flew down and lit on her shoulder, and gentle Maeve stroked and petted it. It kept with her wherever she went, and when Maeve returned to the castle, it flew up in the trees and stayed there to watch for her coming again. And every time that Maeve came abroad, the Hawk flew down upon her shoulder. And when at last it discovered Maeve's chamber window, it flew in at night and nestled in her bosom as she slept.

Word spread about the wonderful bird that had come to be a comrade to Maeve; and the Queen heard of it, and soon also learnt that the bird was the Prince of Greece himself. She sent word of the Hawk's wooing to her evil sister who then worked her spells that turned the Hawk into a Hound.

But now, whenever Maeve went out, there was a lovely Hound awaiting her. It put its feet on her shoulders, kissed her, and licked her face, and the gentle Maeve stroked and petted it, and with Maeve it journeyed wherever she went. Always it was with her, hither and thither, and she fondling it. At length it followed into the castle, and lay and slept at night across the threshold of her chamber.

The castle servants began talking about the Hound, and in short time it reached the ears of the Queen, who knew that it was the Prince of Greece. She sent word to her sister, who then turned the Hound into a green Linnet. And the sister advised the Queen to imprison Maeve in the topmost room of the highest tower of the castle, with only bread and water for food and drink, till she would pine away and die. Then Maeve was imprisoned in the topmost room of the castle's highest tower—from where the Queen every day expected to hear that she was pining to her death.

The Linnet homed in the trees around the castle, and sang there, and waited to see Maeve come out for walking. But Maeve, alas, never came! The Linnet kept flying and flying from tree to tree, watching and waiting, and singing and singing, in hope to see or to attract Maeve—but never once could it catch a glimpse of her.

Until, at last one day, sitting and singing on a tree underneath the tower, it glanced up and caught glimpse of Maeve's small white hand fluttering a handkerchief to it from between the bars of the high window.

There was one very tall poplar tree growing by the tower, whose top reached close to Maeve's window. Up to the topmost branch of the poplar tree the green Linnet flew, rejoicing, and sang and sang all day to Maeve, and flew in of her window at night, and slept nestling in her bosom. And every day and every night after this, the same it did. And the Linnet and Maeve were as happy as the day was long, and the night peaceful.

Every day the Queen was inquiring of the servant whose duty it was to bring her bread and water to Maeve, if she was losing her beauty and pining to her death. But to her surprise and anger, she was hearing the servant every new day report that Maeve was getting rosier, brighter, and lovelier than she had ever been before, and the eyes of her sparkling with joy.

Then the Queen had a watch set, and discovered that the Linnet was sitting and singing to Maeve from the poplar tree, through the day, and nestling in her bosom at night. Terribly enraged at this, she sent word of it at once to her witch sister. And her sister cast new spells, and turned the poplar tree into a great, hissing, biting serpent, and every branch into a little serpent, hissing and darting and biting. So when the Linnet would perch on the tree to sing to Maeve, the tree and all its branches hissed and dabbed and darted and bit the poor bird, till blood flowed from twenty wounds. Maeve tried to persuade the Linnet to go away and save itself, but so great was its love for Maeve that it wouldn't do so. When at length it looked as if the poor bird must bleed to death, Maeve remembered the Yellow River of All Healing, that flowed in the mountains a hundred miles from the castle, told the Linnet of it, and sent it away to get healed.

The Linnet flew off to the Yellow River of All Healing; and when it was bathing its poor mangled body in the waters, the Queen's evil sister came to it and offered, if it would give up Maeve and marry Sorcha, to turn it back into its own handsome and happy Prince-shape again—and on the marriage day she would bestow on him a gold mine in the mountains. But the Linnet would not listen, and said it would sooner suffer a hundred years and sing to its true love, Maeve, than marry Sorcha and get with her the full of a world of gold.

After bathing in the River of All Healing, the Linnet was completely recovered and flew back to the castle and to the hissing, biting poplar tree, where it sat and sang even sweeter than before to Maeve in her tower room. But the tree hissed and darted and dabbed, and bit the poor bird till soon it was covered with wounds, was worse than before, and ready to drop. Then Maeve begged of it to go again to the Yellow River of All Healing. Again it flew there; and when it was bathing in the River of All Healing, the evil woman came and tried to bribe and to tempt it, and offered to give it, not only its own shape as Prince of Greece again, but likewise a whole mountain of gold on the day it would marry Sorcha. But the Linnet scorned her offer and would not listen or heed. And when it had bathed and was recovered, it flew back once more to the castle and to the poplar tree, where it lit on the topmost branch and began singing enchantingly to Maeve in her tower room.

The poplar tree and its branches hissed, and dabbed, and darted, and bit, and tore at the poor Linnet till it was near to death. On Maeve's command it started off once more for the Yellow River of All Healing. But so weak and so ill it was from loss of blood, and so sorely suffering from its myriad wounds, that it dropped and fell a hundred times on the way, and barely reached the River—for the last mile its wings dragging, trailing itself along the ground. Barely the last bit of life was left in its body, and the last drop of blood in its heart, when it reached the River.

When the evil woman tempted it this day, it was weary, and worn, and heartsick-and-sore, yet refused her offer, saying that as Maeve was its heart's love, her it could never forget; and if it wedded another, it would never know a happy hour because of its thoughts and regrets for lovely, sweet Maeve.

The evil woman said she would relieve it of its heart pain and had power to give it forgetfulness, so that thought of Maeve would never again trouble its mind.

So weary and worn and heart-sore was the poor Linnet, and so sure that it never could survive another hour on the cruel poplar tree, that at length it gave in to be turned into its own shape again as Prince of Greece and take Sorcha to that country. But on condition that he should not marry Sorcha for a trial seven years and a day, to find if, for sure, thought of Maeve would not come again and make life a dread burden unto him. The evil woman agreed to the condition and turned him into his own shape, the handsome young Prince of Greece. And he took Sorcha with him to his own country.

For lee and long, Maeve in her tower waited and watched for the return of her Linnet. But it never returned! She began to pine and to fail. And at long and at last, from the servant who brought her bread and water she learned the news that made her heart sore. After that she thought and thought, and planned and contrived, till she managed to make her escape from the tower and from the castle. She started to walk the world and seek out her Prince—who was now reigning King of Greece.

Over hills and dales she went, seeking and searching—over mountains and plains, over broad lands and waters wide. Through great countries she trudged, and over vast oceans she sailed, for weeks, for months, for weary, weary years. Her feet were bruised and broken and bleeding, her clothes were faded and ragged. But never stop nor stay from her search did she, till at last, after years of suffering and journeyings dread, she reached Greece—and on a bright morn caught sight of the King's castle. To a river that flowed past the castle grounds she went, to bathe her bleeding feet in the welcome waters.

It happened that the castle's washerwomen were at the river washing clothes; and they gabbled, all excited, about the wonderful wedding that was to come off three days from now—the young King to be wedded to Princess Sorcha whom he had brought from Ireland seven years before. And she heard them tell how messengers were out over Greece and neighboring countries, inviting kings and queens, and princes and nobles and knights to this wonderfullest wedding that Greece ever had known or would know.

Hearing this, Maeve sat her down on the river bank, her elbows on her knees, and her head in her hands, sobbing sore. She found a hand put on her shoulder and, looking up, saw a little old woman leaning on a stick, who looked kindly into her eyes and said, "Princess Maeve from Ireland, why do you cry?" Then Maeve told the kind, little old woman her story.

Then the little woman said, "Dry your tears, beautiful Maeve, and I will do what I can to help you. Here," says she, "are three golden eggs," and she gave three shining golden eggs to Maeve. "Take these and do with them as I direct you." She said, "The Princess Sorcha walks in the castle park for an hour every day with the young King, wooing him to a wedding that his heart isn't in. At noon, they sit them down on a marble seat under the rowan tree in the garden's center, and Sorcha, to win his heart, says in his ear all the alluring things she can think of. Though

Sorcha's courting him has gone on for seven years, she hasn't yet won the King's heart—even though he is marrying her to keep a promise he made when he brought her from Ireland. You must go into the park at noon each day for the next three days, and walk by the marble seat where they are sitting, and as you pass, each day let an egg drop and break at their feet, and then follow all my directions." And full directions what then to do she gave to Maeve, and Maeve thanked her, and the little old woman leaving with Maeve the lovely eggs, went away.

At noon that day Maeve was in the castle park, and on the marble seat under the rowan tree she saw Sorcha sitting with the handsome young King of Greece and speaking to his ear. Maeve walked past the seated pair and let drop one of the golden eggs. It smashed at their feet, and from it appeared a tiny little maiden, sitting spinning silver thread upon a lovely, golden spinning wheel!

The seated pair looked at this joy and wonder. "Young woman," says Sorcha to Maeve, whom she didn't, couldn't recognize because she was so worn and torn—"Young woman," says she, "what will you take, and let me have that lovely spinner and her wheel?"

And Maeve answered her, "You can have it if you let me have your place at the young King's side for an hour."

Sorcha gladly consented, but before leaving the King's side slipped on his shoulders a Cloak of Sleep. And as Maeve sat down by him, he was in deep sleep. But Maeve then sang in his ear:

> "My love, my young Prince,
> My World of all Worlds,
> My Hawk of Kindness,
> My Hound of Fondness,
> And my darling little Singing Linnet,
> I have swam the seas to you,
> I have climbed the hills to you,
> I have crossed a thousand plains,
> I have dragged me here all weary, weary,
> And now my heart lies bleeding at your feet!"

Over and over and over again, in the King's ear softly she sang the sad song—till the hour was up—with no effect, no slightest sign of response to lift her heavy heart.

"What was the strange woman saying to you?" Sorcha—who had been all the time watching, jealous, from behind a tree—asked when she took her place again at the King's side, slipping from his shoulders the Cloak.

Said he, "She's some poor crazy girl, alas. I was asleep and like a dream I could dimly hear her rhyming over and over some nonsensical chant that had no meaning to me!"

"That's very odd," says Sorcha.

Very well and good. Next day at noon, as the two were sitting down on the marble seat, along came Maeve again, and, passing them, dropped the second golden egg. It broke at their feet, and from it sprang two tiny weavers with little golden looms, on which they weaved a web of silver and gold.

Sorcha looked in wonder and admiration at the lovely sight.

"Oh, strange young woman," says Sorcha, says she, "what will you take and let me have the wee weavers and looms?"

And Maeve said, "Your place at the King's side for an hour."

Sorcha agreed and gave her place to Maeve. But before leaving the King, she slipped on his shoulders the Cloak of Sleep. And he was deep a-sleeping when Maeve sat down by him. Again she began singing in his ear:

> "My love, my young Prince,
> My World of all Worlds,
> My Hawk of Kindness,
> My Hound of Fondness,
> And my darling little Singing Linnet,
> I have swam the seas to you,
> I have climbed the hills to you,
> I have crossed a thousand plains,
> I have dragged me here all weary, weary,
> And now my heart lies bleeding at your feet!"

Till the hour was ended, she sang without getting a single response, and had to leave again with heavy, heavy heart.

"What was the strange young woman saying to you?" Sorcha asked him when she came back from behind her tree and slipped off him the Sleep Cloak.

"Oh," says the King, says he, "the poor woman must be astray in her mind, Lord help her! She was rhyming over and over and over again some nonsense rhyme, whatever it is. No sense could I make of it."

Yet his mind began puzzling and wondering.

Well and good. That passed, and it came to the next day, the third and last. For the great wedding was to be celebrated this evening. On this day as Sorcha and the King sat on the seat under the rowan tree, along came Maeve once more, and, passing them, dropped at their feet the third golden egg—out of which sprang a little golden coach, with coachman, footmen, and four wee, beautiful prancing black horses, their harness of shining silver and gold, sparkling with diamonds and jewels.

The young King and Sorcha looked at the lovely sight in wonder and admiration.

"Oh, strange young woman," says Sorcha, says she, entranced, "what will you take and let me have that beautiful thing?"

"An hour at your King's side," says Maeve. And Sorcha agreed, but would slip the Cloak of Sleep on the King's shoulders before leaving him.

Now the young King, who had been wondering and wondering, and thinking and thinking over the strange happenings, and, recollecting that, each day, Sorcha had slipped a cloak on him before leaving, made up his mind to know more about the meaning of it all. So he let the cloak slip from his shoulders as Maeve took her place by his side and began crooning in his ear:

> "My love, my young Prince,
> My World of all Worlds,
> My Hawk of Kindness,
> My Hound of Fondness,
> And my darling little Singing Linnet,
> I have swam the seas to you,
> I have climbed the hills to you,

I have crossed a thousand plains,
I have dragged me here all weary, weary,
And now my heart lies bleeding at your feet!"

The first time she sang it, the King was startled by something waking in his mind. When she repeated the rhyme, he, listening hard, found memories stirring and growing. He said, "Young woman, sing that song again."

She sang it again—and he, excited, cried, "Again!"

And when once more she sang it, he gave a cry of joy and clasped the ragged girl in his arms!

He looked in her face and remembered—remembered everything! He embraced and kissed Maeve and led her to the castle, both of them now crying for joy. He called for his Commanders to take Sorcha away and convey her back to her mother in Ireland, and had Maeve dressed in satins and silks, the finest the castle could produce. And when that was done, all the Court were in wonder at her dazzling loveliness. And all the kings and queens, and nobles and knights, and ladies and gentlemen, who were now arriving for his wedding to Sorcha, when they beheld the beauty of Maeve, were overcome with wonder and delight.

That evening the beautiful young King of Greece and the beautiful Princess Maeve of Ireland were married before the greatest and most brilliant throng that ever came together in the kingdom of Greece. The wedding lasted nine days and nine nights and the last day was better than the first day. And the King of Greece and his beautiful Queen Maeve ruled over Greece as King and Queen for many and many a long and happy, happy year.

THE KING
WHO WAS A GENTLEMAN

A KING there was in Munster of Ireland's south, long, long ago, who was a very great gentleman. In fact, he was the greatest gentleman in all the world because, in all his life, he had never once said, "You're a liar," to any man.

Now all the world began wondering, and all the world began talking about such a wonderful gentleman who could never be provoked into using these rude words. And the King grew proud and then vain of the fact that he was, thereby, the one greatest gentleman in the world.

So vain did he become of his great gentlemanliness that he invited anyone in all the world to come and test him. He offered to give three chances to anyone who came to try to provoke him into saying, "You're a liar." And so sure of himself was he that, to encourage them to come, he made offer that if anyone in all the world in one of three chances could provoke him into saying the rude words, he would give to that man his beautiful daughter

—the most beautiful maiden in all the world—in marriage, with her weight in gold and half of his kingdom.

But, on the other hand, it was to be agreed that if anyone came there and took the three chances at the King and failed to make him say the rude words, that man's head should be cut off and placed on a spike in front of the King's castle. Now around this castle was a great railing with three hundred and sixty-five spikes on it; and at the time this story begins—for this is only the last of a series of three hundred and sixty-five stories—there were three hundred and sixty-four men's heads sitting on three hundred and sixty-four spikes, and just one spike craving for a head. They were the heads of three hundred and sixty-four nobles and knights, and kings and chiefs, and princes and scholars who had come there thinking they could provoke that wonderful gentleman into using the rude words, and win his beautiful daughter with her weight in gold and half of his kingdom. But every one of them had failed and lost his head—three hundred and sixty-four of them!

Now at this time there lived in the mountains of Donegal, in the North, a poor widow woman who had one son called Jack. A fine, brave, stout, strapping, able fellow was Jack, and when he grew up to be man-big, he rose up by the fireside one night and told his mother about the wonderful gentleman King in the South, and the wonderful offer he had made to any man who could provoke him into saying, "You're a liar!"

Jack said, "Mother, if you'll give me your blessing, I'll travel away to the South of Ireland, and I'll make the King say, 'You're a liar,' and I'll win his beautiful daughter with her weight in gold and half his kingdom."

When his mother heard this, she clasped Jack to her bosom and she begged of him, "Jack, Jack, dear, don't go for to do such a foolish thing! Don't you know that, already, three hundred and sixty-four of the greatest nobles and knights, kings and chiefs, princes and scholars have gone there, believing that they could make that King say the rude words, but because he's the greatest gentleman in all the world, all of them failed and lost their heads, so how do you think that a poor, ragged, ignorant boy like you from the mountains of Donegal could succeed, where the greatest, the wisest, and the most learned men in all the world have failed?"

Jack said, "Mother, I believe that with the Lord's blessing and your blessing, I could make that King say 'You're a liar.' I think I have the Lord's blessing, and I'm only waiting for yours."

And Jack was so persistent that his poor mother, at length, broken-hearted, had to give him her blessing and let him go.

Jack set out from home and he traveled away and away, far farther than I could tell you, and twice farther than you could tell me, till at long and at last he reached the castle of the King who was the greatest gentleman in all the world. He knocked on the gates and the King, himself, came there and asked Jack, "Who are you, or what do you want?" Jack said, "I am Jack, the widow's son, from Donegal. I have heard that you are the most wonderful gentleman in all the world, who never yet said to any man, 'You're a liar.' I have heard how you have offered your beautiful daughter in marriage, with her weight in gold and half your kingdom, to anyone who in one of three chances can make you say the rude words. And here I am, to try my luck on you."

The King, he smiled down upon Jack and said, "Jack, did you notice anything peculiar as you came up to my castle?"

Jack said, "I did."

"What was it?" said the King.

Said Jack, "I noticed three hundred and sixty-four heads sitting on three hundred and sixty-four spikes around your castle—which I thought peculiar."

"It was," said the King. "And, Jack, did you notice anything else?"

"I did," said Jack. "I noticed one spike waiting for a head."

"Now Jack," said the King, "you're a brave lad, and I so like the looks of you that I'd hate to be coming out of my castle every morning and looking you in the face with your head stuck on a spike there. Consequently, Jack," he said, "I advise you to go back home with your head safe on your shoulders and don't take those three chances at me. Because, Jack," he said, "I want to tell you that I am the greatest gentleman in all the world and can assure you that no man in all the world could, under any circumstances, provoke me into forgetting my gentlemanliness and using the rude words."

Jack, he might have let himself be persuaded, but at that instant wasn't there a window thrown open in the castle, and Jack, gazing up, saw looking out of the window the rarest vision he had ever seen in all his life! It was the King's beautiful daughter, herself! She looked down at Jack and she smiled on him, and her smile lit up half the world. And Jack, that instant, fell head over heels in love with that beautiful maiden.

And he said to the King, "If I had a thousand heads instead of only one, I'd gladly risk them all for sake of such a beautiful Princess as that! I want you to give me my three chances at you."

The King smiled down upon Jack, and he said, "Jack, you certainly are a brave fellow, and why shouldn't you have your three chances at me as well as the best o' them? Come," he said, "Come in." And he led Jack within the gates.

"Now, Jack," he said, "You have come a long journey and you must be both tired and hungry. I think we'll put off my test till morning. In the meantime, Jack," he said, "go to the castle kitchen and get a good supper and a soft bed for the night."

Jack, you may be sure, didn't let much grass grow under his heels till he was in the castle kitchen, where he got the father and mother of a good supper. And then a bed in the castle—a feather-bed—and Jack, who had been used to lying on the hard floor at home, sank in it so deep that he thought it would take him three weeks to find his way out again! Right hearty sleep he had, and in the morning, after the greatest breakfast of his life, the King came to him and said, "Well, Jack, are you ready?" And Jack said, "Yes, ready." The King said, "Then come with me for your three chances. For your first chance, come with me out to my stables, and I'll show you some horses that I'm rather proud of. After I've shown you these horses you can take your first chance at trying to provoke me into using the rude words."

The King led Jack out to his stables and there showed him the most wonderful sight of horses Jack ever saw or dreamt of in all his life. There were three hundred and sixty-five horses standing in three hundred and sixty-five stalls, and every horse of them was thirty-nine feet high! And the King said, "Jack, what do you think of them horses of mine?"

Now Jack, before he left his home in the mountains of Donegal, had never seen anything great in all his life. But when he set out he knew that he would be seeing, in the south of Ireland, the greatest wonders the world knew, and he made up his mind as he came along that he wouldn't pretend to wonder at anything at all, at all—but let on that he had been used to just as great things at home.

So my brave Jack didn't pretend to wonder at all, at all, outside of himself. But, seeing a grand chance of making the King say, "You're a liar," he looked up at the King and said, "Oh, King, I suppose they're brave little ponies for the south of Ireland, but nothing at all compared to the horses my father used to keep at his castle at home in Donegal."

But that gentlemanly King, instead of saying, "You're a liar," just smiled down upon Jack and asked, "Jack, what kind of wonderful horses were them your father used to keep in Donegal?"

And Jack, to make the most of his first chance, and determined to provoke the King into saying the rude words, went on, "Oh, King, it beats me to describe what them horses of my father's were like—but there was one little pony among them, a pet of mine, that I want to tell you about. That little pony was only nineteen mile high, and I used to mount him by a step-ladder that was half mile from step to step. And now," said Jack, sure that he had the King, "what do you think of that little pony of mine?"

But that King, instead of saying, "You're a liar," just smiled down upon Jack and said, "Jack, I think that was a wonderful pony, entirely."

And Jack had lost his first chance!

"Now Jack," said the King, "for your second chance, come with me out in the garden till I show you some wonderful bees I have there. If you didn't wonder at my horses, you're going to have to wonder at these wonderful bees of mine."

He led Jack into the garden, and there Jack saw the most wonderful sight of bees that ever he had seen in all his life before. There were three hundred and sixty-five bee *skeps* (hives), and each bee *skep* was the size of a school house, and every bee flying out from there was the size of a goose! And the King, very proud of his wonderful bees, looked down at Jack and said, "Jack, what do you think of them bees of mine?"

But Jack didn't pretend to wonder at all, at all, outside of himself. But sure that he could now make the King say, "You're a liar," he looked up and said, "Oh, King, I suppose they're brave little midges for the south of Ireland, but they're nothing at all to the bees that my father used to keep at his castle in Donegal." —And he watched to see if the King would say, "You're a liar." But that King was only smiling down at him and asked what those bees were like. And Jack, to make the most of his second chance, hurried on, and said, "Oh, King, it beats me to describe what them bees were like. But there was one bee among them, the Queenie Bee of them all, that I want for to tell you about. That Queenie Bee my father always had to keep chained at home because whenever she went abroad the wind of her wings destroyed forests and overturned towns and cities."—And he turned the tail of his eye on the King, but the King was smiling more and more; and he hurried on, to make the most of his second chance. And he said, "There was one time the Queenie Bee burst her chains and got away and flew over to Scotland, and the King of Scotland soon sent word to my father to come over with his army and bring back his murderous Queenie Bee. At that time," Jack said, "our army was scattered to the ends of the earth, and my father ordered me to gather up as many stragglers as I could and go over to Scotland and bring back the Queenie Bee. I could only gather nine millions, nine hundred and ninety-nine thousand men, but I mounted my little pony, only nineteen mile high, and headed that handful of men away for Scotland.

"When I came to the shores of Ireland, lo and behold you! I hadn't a boat to bring my army over the sea to Scotland. So what do you think I did? I put my little pony at the sea, and with his two forefeet he thrashed the sea dry all the way from Ireland to

Scotland, and that army of nine million, nine hundred and ninety-nine thousand men marched from Ireland to Scotland without wetting a shoestring! And when I came there, I borrowed the King of Scotland's army, along with my own, and I borrowed nine thousand miles of chains, and we surrounded and chained the Queenie Bee and dragged her home to Ireland. And now, oh, King," he said, looking up at the King, "what do you think of that Queenie Bee of my father's?"

Jack was sure he now had the King, who couldn't help himself but *must* say "You're a liar." But such a very great gentleman was that King that instead of saying, "You're a liar," he just smiled down at Jack and said, "Jack, I think that was a wonderful Queenie Bee, entirely."

And Jack had lost his second chance!

"Now, Jack," the King said, "I'm a very busy man, and I'm only wasting my valuable time with you. Come along till I give you your third and last chance, and that we get the head chopped off you and have done with you. And," he said, "for your third and last chance, come out into my fields till I show you some beans I have grown there that I'm rather proud of. If I couldn't make you wonder at my horses or my bees, you're going to have to wonder at these beans."

And he led Jack out in the fields and showed him there a field of beans the like of which Jack had never seen or dreamt of in all his life. Every stalk grew the height of the castle, and every leaf would cover a house, and every bean was the size of Jack's head! And the King, mighty proud of his beans, said, "Now, Jack, what do you think of them beans of mine?"

Jack didn't pretend to wonder at all, at all, outside of himself, and he said, "Oh, King, I suppose they're brave little peas for the south of Ireland, but they're nothing at all compared to the beans my father used to grow at his castle at home in Donegal," and he

And the King, very proud of his wonderful bees, looked down at Jack and said, "Jack, what do you think of them bees of mine?"

looked up, thinking the King would say "You're a liar," but the King only smiled down on Jack and said, "Jack, what kind of beans was them your father used to grow in Donegal?"

Now Jack, finding himself on his last legs, was resolved to make the most of his last chance, and the brave fellow said to himself, "I'll make the King say 'You're a liar' this time, or I'll perish."

He said, "Oh, King, it beats me to describe what them beans of my father's were like. But there was one bean stalk that grew in my father's field that I want to tell you about. That bean stalk grew so high above the clouds that we never knew its height— but my father used to engage nine thousand harvest men to climb the stalk and harvest the beans. They would always start up on Easter Sunday, reach above in September, and after shaking down the beans, be down on earth again in time to eat their Christmas dinner."

And sure that he had the King now, who must say, "You're a liar" to that, he looked up to have the joy of seeing him come out with the rude words. But, such a great gentleman was that King, that instead of saying, "You're a liar," he was smiling benevolently down upon Jack. And Jack found his head trembling upon his shoulders!

But he was such a brave fellow that he resolved to make the most of what was left of his third chance and he said to himself, "I'll make the King say 'You're a liar' or I'll perish." And he hurried on, and he said, "There was one time, after I had finished my schooling and it was ordered that I should travel for three years to finish my education, when my father asked me what country of all the world I would like to travel in, and I said, 'Father, I would like to travel up the bean stalk.'

"My poor father begged and beseeched of me to go to any wondrous country in the world, but not ask to go up the bean stalk. But it was the bean stalk or nowhere for me. So I persisted and insisted until my poor father, broken-hearted, had to consent and let me go.

"'Tis well I remember the morning I started—a beautiful, bright, spring morning it was. My father was there crying over me, and he gave me his blessing. And as I started up the bean stalk he said, 'Jack, Jack, dear, don't forget to write.'

"Up and up the bean stalk I went until, what do you think, but when I was nine-hundred-and-ninety-nine thousand miles up the bean stalk I missed my footing and down I fell! I was five months falling. Around the bottom of the beanstalk was a solid rock—and I fell so far and fell so fast that I sank up to my neck in the solid rock."

That was the climax and Jack now knew he had the King where he must say, "You're a liar," and looked up to have the joy of seeing the King say it. But, behold, such a wonderful gentleman was that King that instead of saying "You're a liar," he was smiling more benevolently than ever down upon Jack! And Jack now felt his head shaking from his shoulders.

But such a brave fellow was he that he resolved to make the most of the last shadow of a chance that remained; and he said to himself, "I'll make the King say 'You're a liar' yet or I'll perish!"

And he went on. And he said, "I looked around to see could I get any help to help me out, but couldn't see soul or sinner on all the horizon. And after I was seven years stuck there, I got so tired of it all that I put my hand in my pocket, pulled out my knife, cut off my head, and sent it home to look for help to help me out." There he stopped and looked up for the joy of seeing the King say "You're a liar."

But behold you, such a great gentleman was he, that King, that instead of saying "You're a liar," the fellow was smiling more provoking than ever down upon Jack. And Jack now found his life lost—almost.

But such an undaunted lad was he that he resolved to make the most of the last shadow of a shade of a chance, and he said to himself, "I'll make the King say 'You're a liar,' yet, or I'll perish"—and went on.

He said, "When I sent my head home to look for help, I was watching after my head, going across the country."

That was the climax! And he had the King now, at last, for certain—so he up-glanced for the final joy of it all.

But behold, such a great gentleman was that King that, instead of saying "You're a liar," he was smiling as he never had smiled. And *that* was the final end of Jack. He could feel the head tumbling off him!

But lo and behold! such a wonderfully brave fellow was he that he resolved to make the most of the last shadow of a shade of a shade of the ghost of a chance, and he said to himself, "I'll make the King say 'You're a liar,' yet, or I'll perish!"

And he went on.

He said, "As I was watching after my head going across the country, what do you think did I see? As the head of me was passing under a hill half a mile off, I saw a fox jump out of a bush on top of the hill and come leaping, jumping, bounding down the hill, making for my poor head. And when he got there, the fox gave one jump on top of my poor head, and began to worry it. And so mad did that murderous fox make me that I got a good grip of myself and with both hands, I gave a long pull and a strong pull, pulled myself clean out of the rock, and ran to the help of my head. And when I got there, so mad was I with that beast that I lifted my foot and gave him three kicks, and every kick I gave him I knocked out of him a King, and every King of them," Jack said, looking up defiant, "was a far finer and a far better and a far greater gentleman than you!"

"YOU'RE A LIAR!!" cried the King, black and blue in the face with rage!

You see, Jack had early learned the King's weak spots—his vanity about being the greatest gentleman in all the world; and he had been playing the King along, till he had him off his guard, and then struck him on the weak spot and got his results!

For the raging King, dancing mad, repeated, "You're a liar! And you're the greatest liar that ever walked in all the world!"

It was now Jack's turn to smile. He looked up at the King and said, "True words for your Royal Highness—I'm a liar, and a great one—but I'm the son-in-law of the greatest gentleman in all the world!"

And sure enough, when the King cooled and came to himself, he had to confess that Jack was the best and the bravest and the noblest fellow ever he had come across, and he would sooner see him married to his daughter than any of the three hundred and sixty-four nobles and knights, and kings and chiefs, and princes and scholars who had come trying to win her.

More by the same token, when the beautiful Princess herself came on the ground, she confessed that the minute she looked out of the window and saw Jack at the gates, she had fallen head over heels in love with him. He was the only one of all the three hundred and sixty-five nobles and knights, and kings and chiefs, and princes and scholars that she had loved—the only one she could have married.

Jack, before he married her, went back home and brought his poor old mother here with him. Then the King sent out the invitations for the wedding and he asked all the knights and nobles and ladies and gentlemen, and that was the greatest wedding known before or since. He asked in all the kings and queens, and princes and chiefs, and nobles and ladies. That wedding feast lasted ninety-ninety days and ninety-nine nights, and the last day and night were finer and greater and more enjoyable than the first. The King divided his kingdom with Jack, who, with the bride, was crowned. And they lived happy and well ever after.

NANNY AND CONN

THERE were, once on a time, a poor woman and her man named Nanny and Conn, who, despite poverty, lived quiet and agreeable together, in peace, comfort, and content, though childless, for many years. One day Conn, coming from the potato field to get a bit of breakfast, found my brave Nanny sitting in the chimney corner surrounded by a bunch of neighbor women, all of them crying and whillelewing and pillelewing like the End of the World was coming up the road. "Why, Nanny, Nanny," says Conn, says he, "What's the matter with you? And what ails everybody? Or is my house become a crazy house?"

"Och, och, Conn, Conn darling!" says Nanny. " 'Tis me has the sore heart this morning! Do you know, Conn, dear, that 'tis drawing on fifty years again' Patrickmas since we were made man and wife, and yet Providence hasn't sent us a son to be a comfort to us in our old age! Och, Conn, Conn darling!" says she, "but 'tis the sore pity of me this morning! Ochón! Ochón!"

"Well by my boots," says Conn, "but that bangs Banagher!

Such foolishness I never knew, and I'm a middling-old man."
And with that Conn turned on his heel and away out he goes to
his work again, breakfastless. The brave Conn wrought hard at
his work till it was fair dinnertime, and then, sticking his spade
in the ridge, he started for the house again, wondering to himself
if Nanny had done pining for the son she never saw. But when
Conn put his foot on the door-threshel, there sat Nanny on one
side the fire, a neighbor woman on the other, and a third in the
middle, with no sign of pot or pan on it, nor dish or spoon on
the table, but the three women of them—Och! Och! Och!—
keening and ochóning, one louder than another, fit to lift the
roof!

Conn put a sigh out of him, sat down on a creepy stool, his
chin on his fists, and his elbows on his knees, and he looking dis-
tractedly from the one to the other. When he'd let them get a
bit out of breath and found opportunity, says he, quiet and easy-
like, "Ma'am, haven't ye yet done with your foolish honing because you didn't get a child?"

"Och, no, Conn, Conn, Conn darling!" says Nanny. "That's
not what we're crying about now at all, but—och! och! och!
ochón! Conn darling, Conn dear!—it's something far, far worse!"

"Well, in troth," says Conn, relieved, "I'm glad to know it's
worse.—What is it, Nanny?"

"Oh Conn, Conn darling," cries Nanny, "great disaster entirely has come in the house since you left it. Do you see that corn-
riddle there that fell, one hour ago, from the loft overhead?" she
said, pointing to a riddle capsized on the floor. The women
edged away from it like it was a plague.

"Well, well, well!" says Conn, distracted. "If the falling down
of a corn-riddle is the disaster which you and your troop are
crying all your eyes out for, I don't know whether to laugh or
cry myself, or to take down the stick and wallop the bunch of
ye!"

"Och, och, och, och! But Conn darling, you don't under-
stand," Nanny said. "Don't you see? That spot where the riddle
fell is the identical spot where I had planned for the cradle if the
good Lord had seen fit to send us a baby!—Och! Och! Och!

Och! What's this to do at all! Och! Och! Och! Och!"

Conn looked more and more distracted and dumfounded. "And what then?" says he.

"Och, och, och! How stupid men can be!" Nanny exclaimed, gulping and bursting into a crying fit. And both of her company burst out crying along with her, and chorusing, "How stupid, stupid, men can be!"

Conn thought stupidness must surely have overcome him. But he pleaded to his weeping wife, "Nanny, Nanny dear, stupid I must be, and beginning to doubt whether I'm on my heels or my head. Won't you insense me what the riddle has to do with our deprivation?"

"Och, och, och, och, och!" cries Nanny. "Don't you—can't you—see that, if we had had a child and the child to be in its cradle on that spot where the riddle came crashing—don't you see that our dear, lovely child would now be de–de–de–DEAD!" And she put from her a scream of anguish that nigh raised the roof. And the women put from them such howls of pain that he had to clap both hands on his ears to shut out the noise and hold in his senses.

He dropped down in a seat and buried his head in his hands, till the pillelewing of the women got more civilized, and his power of speech came back to him. Then he said, "I have lived long and traveled far, everywhere between Bundrowish and Bunna-trahan, and witnessed many an unbelievable thing, but the beat of ye for silly women, or even your like, I never yet saw, heard of, or encountered. I'll set out," he said, "this very instant, put my foot to the road, follow my nose, and never come back to you, Nanny, and your three keeners, till I have found— if I ever can find—man, woman, or mortal behaving as silly as you, Nanny. Good-bye"—and off with him, heavy-hearted.

But lo, not far had he traversed till he met up with a crowd of panting, *pighing* men lined along both sides of a great *peiste* (serpent) bound with ropes—the most monstrous he had ever seen—that was plainly breaking both their backs and their hearts with the carrying of it.

"Thank Heaven we meet you!" says the headman of them.

"We sore need your help at this commendable carrying of this destructive beast."

"Where are you going with him?" Conn asked.

"To the sea, nineteen miles off," says the headman. "He's a dangerous destructive brute who lived in our loch for the past hundred years, and has the habit of issuing at night and destroying man and beast. We got him at last and are going to give him the tragic end he has well earned. We're carrying him to the sea, nineteen miles off, to drown him. Lend us a hand, won't you, for he'll have us all killed before we get him killed."

"Lay him down and get me an axe," says Conn.

They wondered, but did as they were bid. And at a few strokes, Conn had his head chopped off.

"Glory be to the Lord of Heaven!" says the men, overcome with wonder. "Who'd ever have thought of it! You must be the most extraordinary genius that ever grew in Ireland. Will you stay with us and be our King?"

Conn, disgusted, gave them the back of his hand and sole of his foot and pushed on.

Next day he came upon a bunch of men in a hay meadow, sitting idle in a circle under a tree, though an acre of hay was outspread and black clouds gathering overhead.

"What's the matter with ye? Are ye going to let your hay spoil?" says Conn.

"It's God's mercy sent you here," says they. "We finished our midday meal here two hours ago, but haven't been able to get up, because, as you see, our legs got mixed, and no man knows whose legs are his and which is some other body's. Can you please sort out our own legs for each of us and extricate us from one another?"

"I'll do that," says Conn, mad. He snatched up an empty bucket that they had unloaded their dinner out of, dipped it in the nearby stream, and dashed it over them, driving every man to leap to his feet with a yell and scatter like crows. Then he went on, shaking his head sadly.

Next day at noon he saw, in a wheatfield where the grain was overripe and falling, a lot of workmen lined up, and one man with a rod counting the line. And when that man finished the count he took his place in the line, and another man, taking the rod, counted the line again. And then another and another. Curious to know the meaning of the strange transaction, he stepped up and asked what the proceeding was all about. The lad with the rod now in his hand who had just finished his count, answered, "We're in great trouble. I wonder if you can help us? You see, our Master sent thirteen of us out here at six o'clock to reap this wheatfield, which is overripe and going to loss. He sent thirteen of us—he counted the thirteen before he started—but when we reached the field and counted ourselves to make sure we were all here, we could get only twelve. Every man of us, in turn, counted the line and could get only twelve, and we've gone on with the counting from morning till now—hoping that surely we'd yet find thirteen, for when we call every man's name, we find everyone here, and none missing. Can you unpuzzle the strange puzzle?" says he.

"Let me see you count them," says Conn. And the lad went down the line, laying the rod on each man's shoulder, till he came to the end of the line. "And now," says he to Conn, in the voice of a man who'd won a victory—"Now, what do you say?"

Says Conn, "But you didn't count yourself!"

"To be sure, I didn't," says he, rebuking-like. "Our Master, when he counted us, didn't count himself."

"Get in the line," says Conn, snapping the rod from him, "till I show you."

The lad got in the line and Conn counted, "One, two, three"—on, till he came to the last man—"thirteen—There you are!"

The eyes of all thirteen near popped from their heads, and they cried out, "A miracle! A miracle!" And they implored Conn, "Can you tell us where did the thirteenth man come from?" But Conn's temper was cracked, and he answered them, "From Hell! And yourselves can go there!" And he departed—whilst they, in a fog of wonder, went on to their reaping.

"I have seen, to my satisfying," says he to himself, turning right around and heading for home.

But he was to meet still more satisfaction on the way back.

He traveled away before him, on and on, and on, getting hungrier every minute, till he came to a cabin, where there was the dirtiest and wrinkledest and wizenedest old hag he ever before saw, she decked with ribbons all colors of the rainbow, sitting on the roadside in front, and singing a love song in a voice that put his teeth on edge. "God save ye, ma'am," says Conn.

"God save yourself, kindly, good man," says she. "Did ye ever see any sign of a King coming down that road?"

"A what?" says Conn.

"A King," says the old hag. "The King of Ireland," says she, "is, I'm told, traveling over the land to find for wife, the beautifullest woman between the four borders, and I'm sitting here waiting till he'll pass, in behopes he might fancy myself. You must know," says she, "that I was told I was the beautifullest girl in the three parishes."

"When was that?" says Conn, "And who told it to you?"

"It was three and sixty years ago," says she, "and the lame beggarman told it to me."

"And how long, my good woman, have you been sitting here, waiting?"

"Against the morrow's morning," says she, "it'll be a year and a day."

"Well, ma'am," says Conn, "I'm the King of Ireland."

"I'd never mistake you for a King," says she.

"That," says he, "is because I'm traveling in disguise. I'm feeling in my bones," says he, "that it's you are the very beautifullest woman I have yet seen or will see, and the one I'd like to pick for my Queen if only I could be sure you can cook a good dinner."

"Oh," says she, joyfully, "come in and let me show you the dinner I can prepare."

And when she'd made and fed hungry Conn the heartiest meal he'd eaten in a month, she said, "Now we can go straight to Father John and get married, for I just can't wait till I'm a Queen."

"You'll have to wait, my sweetheart," says Conn, heading for the door, "till I go home to my castle and get my Sunday silk suit and gold crown, for it would be disgrace for the King of

Ireland to get married in these rags. And my own Bishop I likewise must bring for the wedding."

"I must give you a hug and a sweet kiss," says she, advancing
on him with arms spread.

"Easy, easy," says Conn, backing away. "I'd sooner have the
joy of looking forward for it, after we're married."

"Don't be afeared," she said. "There will be then, more kisses
for you than a schoolmaster could count—I'll kiss you till the
heart of you is bursting with bliss."

She had him, ere he could escape. "Then make it a wee one,"
he said, "for I'll need all my senses going the roads."

But the poor man got a smack that alarmed the echoes on the
hill. And he said a hearty "Thanks be to God!" escaping from
the door. Conn traveled on, and on, and on, till he came to a
house where he found a man and a boy getting underneath a
mule and, with great groaning and moaning, striving to lift it.

"God save ye, and good luck to the work," says Conn.

"God save ye kindly," says the man back to him, "and thank
ye."

"Could I be of any service to ye," says Conn.

"Thank ye kindly," says the man back to him, "ye can that.
My son here and myself are at our last gasp, trying to do what
we're trying to do."

"And what's that?" asks Conn.

Says the man, "It's in regard of them fine bunches of grass ye
see growing out of the roof thatch. It's sinful to see them going
to waste up there. We want to put up the mule till he eats it."

"And," says Conn, says he, "could ye find no more convenient
way of getting the mule to the grass?"

"No," says the man. "We couldn't easy take the roof down to
the mule."

"What do ye think," says Conn, says he, "if I could point you
a way to have your mule eat the grass with less trouble to you?"

Says the man, "If you could do such magic as that, I would
think you a mighty great genius entirely."

"What will you give me if I do it?" says Conn.

"Why," says the man, "I'll tell you. A dozen times every year we have to endure this punishment. I have killed five of my six sons at it already, and this brave lad, my sixth and last, will soon go, too; and I'll be dead myself next with the tragedy of the mule's lifting and holding him up till he gets all the grass eaten. So I'll give ye the mule and his slide-car," says he, "if you can invent an easier plan for him to get to the grass."

"It's a bargain," says Conn, and then and there he told him, "Go up on the house yourself, cut the grass and carry it down and put it to the mule where he stands."

"By the hokey!" cries the man, "You have a head on you! That's the most ingenious plan man or mortal ever thought or heard tell of!"

Then the two helped Conn hook the mule to the slide-car, covered him with their gratitude and started him off. "Well, Nanny," says Conn to himself as he drove along—"Well, Nanny," says he, "there's a few foolisher people in the world than you, anyhow."

He drove on, and on, till after night he came to a wee cabin on the roadside, and, drawing up the mule and the car, he entered and found an old woman on her knees so busy blowing and coaxing the fire to come forward that she didn't notice Conn coming in. Down he sat him on a seat till she'd be done. "Well, *musha* [good luck] on ye for a fire," says she, "that ye won't light; I must put a bit of tallow into ye to humor ye on." And arising she beheld Conn, sitting silent beside her.

"The Lord protect me!" she cried. "Where did *you* come from?"

"From Heaven," says Conn, sarcastic.

"From Heaven!" she exclaimed. "The Lord save us all this blessed night." And when she'd dropped on to a stool, and got her breath with her she said, "From Heaven, do you say? And did you see my man Terence up there?"

"Yes I did, surely," says Conn, to humor her.

"And is he as contentious as he always was here?" she asked.

"Troth and he is," says Conn. "Both contentious and cantankerous—there isn't a door in Heaven he hasn't kicked in smithereens."

"That's him!" says she. "That's him! That's my Terence, sure enough! Tchuck! Tchuck! Tchuck!" says she. "Howling for more whiskey, I suppose?"

"The very thing," says Conn. "How did you know?"

"Ah, poor Terence," says she, "was always fond of the wee drop. I suppose I'll have to send him up some. Is any allowed in?"

"Most certainly, ma'am," says Conn, getting real interested. "They must allow it in for him, or he won't leave a sound board in the whole establishment."

"Oh, every stick and stave," says she. "That's him. That's Terence. I have just got a wee five gallon here," says she. "Do you think you could manage it up with you?"

"Anything to oblige you, ma'am—and preserve Heaven for the rest of us," says Conn. "I have a mule and a slide-car down with me."

"Oh then, if ye have," says she, "maybe ye could fetch him some other little things, too."

"With the greatest of pleasure, ma'am," says Conn.

"Does Terence complain of the cold?" says she.

"He's just perishing with it, ma'am," says Conn.

"Oh, that's just Terence for ye," says she, "he was never done complaining of the cold. Do ye think ye could take him up his overcoat?"

"I'd be only too delighted," says Conn.

"Is he as fond of butter as ever?" says she.

"He can't get enough of it," says Conn.

"Oh, that's just him," says she. "Ye'd better take him that little firkin of it."

"Surely, ma'am," says Conn.

"He used to be mighty partial to a rasher of bacon," says she.

"He's shouting and yelling," says Conn, "for a rasher and eggs yonder every morning he arises."

"Poor man, poor fellow!" says she. "Just take to him that side of a pig hanging in the smoke. And here's a couple of dozen eggs, too—if I'm not troubling you too much, good man," says she.

"Don't mention trouble, please," says Conn.

"Then I might be after asking ye to take poor Terence a few other little things?"

"The more the merrier, ma'am," says Conn. "As far as the mule can draw—and the same animal can haul a hefty lot. And after that, pile on to myself!" says he.

"I must say," says she, stirring herself to get together piles of eatables and drinkables and clothes—"I must say," says she, "you're the most kind, obliging man I've met up with in a month of Sundays. May God reward you!" And down with the load.

"Now," says she, "I think that should keep Terence's mouth shut and heart in quietude for a while. God speed ye," says she, "and thanky, and tell Terence my regards."

"In Terence's name I thank yourself, good woman," says Conn. "I guarantee Terence won't forget you easy. He'll be mighty thankful for every item of these—when he gets them." And off my brave Conn, with his plunder, started—and went whistling and singing before him, light-hearted as the larks above, who halted their own songs to hearken to him.

From his happy load, too, he was eating and drinking to his heart's content. But lo, as he neared home on an evening, having drawn the mule and cart into a wood where he was preparing to camp for the night, he heard a *theraw* coming down the road, a great angry shouting and scolding; he, after turning his coat for safety, went out, and there came dashing on to him a madman and madwoman armed with sticks and stones, and to his alarm, who should he recognize them to be, when they came near, but the man he got the mule from and the woman who gave him the load. They yelled at him, "Did you see a scoundrel with a mule and a slide-car passing this way?"

Struck instantly to his senses, Conn asked, "Was he about of my size and features and wearing a tattered brown coat?"

Says they, "The rascal was so much your size and features, that we'd almost swear you were him only yours is a grey coat and you haven't a mule and a slide-car."

"And did the fellow murder someone, or what?" says Conn.

"Far worse," says they. Says the man, "He got my mule and

slide-car for insensing me how to make feed to my mule of the grass on my roof—but he didn't tell me, and I didn't work out in my head, that the grass is now a-waste on my hand and a total loss, since I haven't any more a mule to eat it. I want to find the rascal and kill him. I traced him to this good woman's house, who has no sense, and would never discover he robbed her likewise, till I demonstrated it to her."

"Yes," she shouted, waving a pair of tongs in the air, "tell me what way he went, till I kill him first."

"No, but tell *me*, and let me get the first killing of the vagabond," says the man, lifting a big blackthorn.

"Easy, easy, both of ye," says Conn. "Do ye see that white cloud that's sailing up to Heaven—there, to the east'ard?"

"We do," says they. "What's that got to do with it?"

"Well, when him that you're looking for reached this spot, that white cloud came down and surrounded him and his equipage, and whisked them off the earth. If you want to find him you'll have to go to Heaven after. He'll be landed there before nightfall."

"Oh! oh! oh!" says the woman. "May the Lord pardon me. Then sure enough he was an angel, after all!"

"And may the Lord pardon me," says the man. "Only I'm so stupid I should have known he was an angel, for no mortal man could have invented such a wonderful way to get the grass to my mule."

"May the good Lord forgive both of us," says the both together. "We mustn't have, after all, been altogether as wise as our neighbors, all our life, famed us for."

"Amen, amen!" says Conn.

And they both set out for their homes with heads hanging.

And Conn, with his mule and his slide-car and his load of provisions that would lift him out of poverty for many a coming day, headed for his home. And it's Nanny was the delighted woman to welcome both him and what he had with him.

And right well she welcomed his news likewise—for, "Nanny," he said, "though I went from you grumbling, I came back gratified. I labored under the delusion that you were silly, but I've learnt that by comparison with the rest of the world, you must be Solomon himself's eldest daughter. It's myself was the foolish one. But I'm cured. I'm now happy and content, not alone to live with you, but to look up to you with admiration for the remainder of my days."

And that he did. And thereafter Nanny and Conn lived and died the happiest couple that the countryside ever knew.

THE ADVENTURES

OF CIAD

CIAD, Ceud, and Mith-Ceud were the sons of the King of Norway. They were famed, the world over, as brave fellows.

On a day, Ciad said to his father, the King, "Ceud, Mith-Ceud, and myself are celebrated far and wide as great heroes, but do we deserve this? Neither of us has ever done anything great. I'm sorely ashamed of bearing a title I haven't won. I will leave your castle, go away, and prove my right to the title of hero, or if I fail, I will never come back."

The King tried hard to dissuade him, but Ciad would not be dissuaded. Then the King asked him to take the pick of his men to accompany him. But Ciad said, "No."

Early next morning Ciad got his father's blessing, took his arms and his shield, and started off. He went to the seashore and traveled by it.

When he had been traveling hours, he saw a speck far out. It was coming nearer and growing bigger every minute. It was a boat, and, nearer, he saw a woman sitting in it. Soon he saw that she was very beautiful.

The boat came straight toward him. The boat's keel grated on the gravel, and Ciad helped the damsel on shore. He said, "Beautiful One, who are you? Where do you come from? And alone?"

She replied, "Give me your name. I will not reply to your questions unless you are of royal blood."

He said, "I am of royal blood. I am Ciad, son of the King of Norway."

She said, "I am glad of that. I am Dark Eye, daughter of the King of France. From France I have come, but where I go I do not know. For a year and a day I have wandered the seas in this little boat, seeking a champion. A cruel stepmother has laid spell on me, under which I must wander forever, over the seas of the world, unless I can find for her the bottle of Ioca [Ointment of Health], that instantly cures all wounds and restores life to the dead, owned by the Queen of the Island of the Riches of the World. I seek this island, but cannot find it, and can find no one who knows where it is. Already I have put *geasa* [an obligation that cannot be refused without loss of honor] on the twelve greatest champions of the world to find and bring me this bottle —but the twelve have lost their lives in the search. As you are a King's son and a hero, I now put *geasa* upon you to bring me this bottle of Ioca of the Queen of the Island of the Riches of the World, and hand it to me here in three years and a day from now."

Ciad said, "I accept the *geasa*, Dark Eye."

Dark Eye thanked him. He helped her into her boat; she pushed off and sailed away until he lost sight of her. Then Ciad turned and went back to his father's castle and told his father of the adventure and of the *geasa* that had been laid on him.

"My poor boy," his father said, "I am very sorry for you. There are not three in all the world who know where is the Island of the Riches of the World. And even if you found it, you would lose your life in trying to take the bottle of Ioca."

Ciad said that since better men had already lost their lives in the search, it would be no shame for him if he, too, lost his.

His father asked him to take with him nine times nine nines of men.

But Ciad said, "No. I shall not take nine men. Give me a ship and let my brothers Ceud and Mith-Ceud come with me. If it is possible to get the bottle of Ioca of the Queen of the Island of the Riches of the World, I, with Ceud and Mith-Ceud, will get it. If it is impossible, then your nine times nine nines of men would be lost to you, as well as we."

His father gave him his blessing and the best ship in the harbor. And with Ceud and Mith-Ceud, Ciad, on the morrow, set out.

They sailed for three days and three nights without meeting any adventure, and on the morning of the fourth day saw a speck on the sea afar off. Soon they saw it was a ship sailing toward them. As it came nearer they saw it was very large, and, nearer still, saw that in the ship was one person, a giant, greater than any giant in their country.

When the strange ship came beside them, the giant asked Ciad who he was and by what right he dared to sail these waters.

Ciad said, "My name I'm not ashamed of. I am Ciad, son of the King of Norway, a hero. Who are you and by what right do you question me?"

The Giant said, "I am the Giant of the Great Seas, and I allow no ship but mine upon them."

Said Ciad, "If that's your law, it's going to be broken this day."

The Giant raised his spear, and Ciad, without waiting, leaped aboard his ship, spear in hand and shield before him.

He and the Giant of the Great Seas fell to and fought as two men never fought before. Their battling was so loud and so fierce and so terrible that the seals came from the North Seas, and the whales from the deeps of the ocean, and the little red fishes came up from the sea-meadows, and all thronged around to watch the fight. The Giant was brave and a great fighter without doubt; his strength and skill were wonderful, but the courageous spirit of Ciad well matched the Giant's strength and skill. When the sun was two hours above the Eastern waters, they began their fight, and when it was dipping into the Western waters the fight was not ended. But the Giant was weakening, and soon would have been beaten, when he gave three loud calls, and a blue mist came down from the skies and wrapped him and his ship around.

When the mist cleared, the Giant and ship were gone and Ciad was struggling in the water.

Ceud and Mith-Ceud took him aboard and found he was so badly abused and so weak from loss of blood that there was nothing for it but to return home, so home they headed.

At home Ciad lay for seven days with his father's doctors attending him. At the end of that time he got up and asked his father to give him thirty men and another ship, that he, with his brothers, might set out again.

His father would persuade him not to go, but it was of no use. Ciad said if he did not fulfill his *geasa*, he could never hold up his head among men again.

Then he set out with two ships. Ceud, Mith-Ceud, and himself were in one ship, and thirty men in the other.

They now sailed for three days and three nights in the same direction in which they had gone before, and on the morning of the fourth day saw two specks on the waters, far off, coming toward them. These got larger every moment. They were two large ships. When they neared, the boys saw the Giant standing in one, and a host of men in the other. When they closed in, Ciad hailed the Giant of the Great Seas and asked him if he meant battle.

The Giant replied, "If you do not mean battle, I do not."

"Where are you going, then?" Ciad asked.

The Giant said, "I'm going in search of the Riches of the World."

"Where is that to be found?" Ciad asked.

"It's on an island in the Far World," the Giant said, "and is owned by the Queen of the Island of the Riches of the World."

"May we go with you?" Ciad asked.

The Giant agreed to this, and all sailed off.

They sailed away and away, far farther than I could tell you, and more than twice as far as you could tell me, and at long last reached the Island of the Riches of the World.

The Giant said to Ciad, "Send your men on the island first, to demand from its Queen the Riches of the World."

Ciad agreed, and sent his men on the island on a morning. But when night fell they had not come back. Next day Ciad himself landed and went in search of them. In the second valley, he found his thirty men lying in blood. He said, "This is the Giant's deceitful doing."

He went back to his ship and told his two brothers to engage the giant's men, whilst he would engage the giant. They attacked the Giant and his men.

A fiercer and bloodier battle was never fought on sea or land. The noise and the din were so loud and the battling was so fierce that the seals came down from the North Seas, the whales came from the deeps of the ocean, and the little red fishes, too, from the sea-meadows—thronging around the ships to watch the fight. For the length of a day they battled, and when the sun was one hour above the Western waters, Ceud, Mith-Ceud, and the Giant's men were all dead, but Ciad and the Giant still battled. When the rim of the sun was on the waters, the Giant, finding himself weakening, gave three calls. Ciad, seeing the blue mist coming, gave a bound in the air and came down driving his spear to the Giant's heart. And the Giant lay dead.

Ciad, taking with him his two brothers' bodies, went on the island and stood them up against a rock facing the east, their helmets on their heads, and shields and spears in their hands. On the next morning he set out over the island and at night came to a little hut, wherein he found an old hag. He asked her if she had no company.

She said, "Yes, I have plenty of that."

He asked to see her company.

She struck her staff on the hearthstone, and up sprang nine other hags as old and ugly as herself. She struck the staff again upon the hearthstone, and up sprang nine of the most beautiful damsels Ciad had ever beheld.

The hag said, "If you stay with me, you can have your choice of these beautiful damsels for your wife."

But Ciad remembered Dark Eye of France, and remembered his *geasa*, and he said to the hag he would have none of them.

Then the hag struck her staff upon the ground angrily, and they all disappeared.

Ciad asked for supper and a bed for the night, and the old hag gave him the toes and the tongue of a rabbit for supper, a heather bed that scored and tore his flesh, and an old black cat for a bedfellow.

In the morning he told the hag that he was seeking the Queen of this island.

She said, "I am the Queen."

"If that is so," he said, "I demand the bottle of Ioca and the Riches of the World."

"That," she said, "I am glad to tell you, you cannot have."

"If I cannot have it," he said, "I will take your staff and break your old bones."

"It's like a hero to do that," she said, scoffing, "but even if you made meal of my old bones, you wouldn't be any nearer the bottle of Ioca and the Riches of the World."

Ciad asked how that was.

She said, "Feach-An-Chric, the Terrible Man of the Hill, took the bottle of Ioca and the Riches of the World from me two hundred years ago."

"I do not believe it," said Ciad.

She took him outside and showed him on the flagstones the hoof-tracks of the Feach's horses, where last night's rains were still lying in them.

"Where does Feach-An-Chric live?" Ciad asked.

"He lives a third part of the world from here," the hag said.

"How may I get there?" Ciad asked.

"As best you can," said the hag.

"By this and by that," said Ciad, seizing her staff, "I'll make meal of your old bones if you don't direct me."

She took him down to the harbor where lay his ship, took a whistle from her pocket, and blew on it. Then a little red fish appeared on the water.

She said, "Follow that fish and it will lead you to Feach-An-Chric."

Ciad stepped into his ship, hoisted his sails, and went off after the little red fish.

He sailed for long, long days and long, long nights, sailing

over one-third of the whole world, until at length the little fish ran into a wood-bordered bay. Ciad anchored his ship here and went on shore.

He traveled over high mountains and deep valleys for three days and three nights, and on the fourth day found Feach-An-Chric on a hill-side, dividing beef among his men.

Ciad walked up and asked for a bit of the beef.

"By my faith, no!" said Feach-An-Chric. "But now that you're here, I'll save my beef."

"How is that?" said Ciad.

"Because I'll divide you among my men," said Feach-An-Chric, rising up.

"You might not," said Ciad.

Ciad and the Feach fell to and fought.

The Feach was a wild and fearful fighter surely, but the courageous spirit of Ciad made him a better. The noise and din and fierceness of the fight were so great that the boars came down from the hills, the deer came up from the valleys, and the birds came from the woods of the world to watch. But before night fell, Ciad put the Feach down and put a knee on his breast and asked him where he would find the bottle of Ioca and the Riches of the World.

Feach-An-Chric said, "If that is what you came and fought for, I'm sorry for you. I had the bottle of Ioca and the Riches of the World only one night when Feach-An-Chille, the Terrible Man of the Wood, forced them from me."

"I do not believe it," said Ciad.

But the Feach showed him the footprints of Feach-An-Chille, with last night's rains still lying in them.

"And where does Feach-An-Chille live?" asked Ciad.

"He lives a third part of the world from here," said Feach-An-Chric.

"And how may I get there?" Ciad asked.

She said, "Follow that fish and it will lead you to Feach-An-Chric."

"You're a brave man," said Feach-An-Chric, "and I would like to see you succeed."

With the point of his spear he rang three times on his shield, and a wolf-dog came running up.

"Follow that dog," said Feach-An-Chric, "and he will lead you to Feach-An-Chille."

Ciad set out after the dog, and traveled away and away, far farther than I could tell you, and more than twice as far as you could tell me, over hill, height, and hollow, mountain, moor, and scrug, lone valley and green glen, for long and for long, until at length and at last he reached the land of Feach-An-Chille. Traveling on, he came upon a hut and saw Feach-An-Chille himself standing outside. The Feach was leaning against the end of his hut, laughing, and every time the Big Fellow laughed, oak trees fell.

"Why do you laugh?" asked Ciad, when he reached him.

"I'm laughing for the joy of killing you!" said Feach-An-Chille.

"Wouldn't it be wiser to laugh after?" said Ciad.

He raised his spear, and he and the Feach went at the fight. The noise and the din and the fierceness of the fight was such that the boars came down from the hills, the deer came up from the valleys, and the birds from the woods of the world loaded the tree-tops around, watching. If Feach-An-Chric was a great fighter, Feach-An-Chille was far greater; but great as he was, Ciad's courageous spirit was still greater, and when the sun went behind the trees in the West, Ciad put the Feach down.

"You're a brave man," said the Feach, when he was down. "What can I do for you?"

"You can give me the bottle of Ioca and the Riches of the World," said Ciad.

"I cannot," said the Feach. "I'm sorry. I had the bottle of Ioca and the Riches of the World only one night, when the King of Persia and his men took them from me. And now," said the Feach, "if that's what you have come adventuring after, you may as well return home, for you can never get them from the King of Persia."

"Why cannot I?" said Ciad.

"Because," the Feach said, "the King of Persia, when he got them, called together the Seven Wizards of the East, and had them lay spells on him so that no man could conquer him."

"I'm sorry for that," said Ciad, "but I'll not return home; I'll fare on to meet my fate."

Ciad traveled for a long time, and came to a plain that was covered with dead men, and on one of the dead men he saw a gold boot and a silver. The gold boot he tried to pull off him— but the man whom he thought was dead struck him with the silver boot, throwing him flat.

"Who are you?" Ciad asked.

"I am Swift Sword, son of the King of Spain, one blow of whose sword has the power of a thousand men for a thousand years and can blow the seas dry," he said. "This is my army that I brought into the Eastern World, all of whom got killed."

"I am glad to find you," said Ciad, "for I am your cousin Ciad, son of the King of Norway. Come join me on my quest." And to Swift Sword he told his story.

Swift Sword was gladdened at meeting his cousin, and readily joined fortunes with Ciad.

Ciad and Swift Sword set out and traveled far, far, until they came to the Lake of the Singing Shore. They traveled by it until they came to a little house. As they came up to it, they saw a white pigeon fly from the chimney at every step they took.

Ciad thought this very strange and said he would enter and find out what it meant. Inside he saw a beautiful young woman sitting by the fire, in her hand a wand covered with scales. She was plucking scales from the wand, one by one, and flinging them into the fire. From every scale she flung in the fire, a white pigeon sprang and flew up the chimney.

"The blessing of Crom on you," said he. "I am Ciad, son of the King of Norway. I am traveling in search of the King of Persia, to get from him the bottle of Ioca and the Riches of the World. I should like to know the name of the beautiful damsel I am addressing."

She said, "I am Pearl Mouth, daughter of the King of Persia, and am living here alone, far from my country and my people."

"Why is that?" Ciad asked.

She said, "A year ago today I married Blue Gold, son of the King of Africa, and on our marriage day he was carried away by Mountain of Fierceness, son of the King of Greece, and turned into a pigeon in the Eastern Skies. I have sat here since, sending off these messengers to find him. Many thousands have I sent, but not one has come back."

"I am sorry for you," said Ciad.

"And I am very sorry for you," said Pearl Mouth.

"How is that?" said Ciad.

"Because my father, the King of Persia, cannot be conquered by living man. You can never force from him the bottle of Ioca and the Riches of the World."

"Then I'll die in trying," said Ciad.

"Isn't it better to get them and live?" Pearl Mouth said.

"But how can I do that?" Ciad asked.

"If you are a very great hero, there is a chance for you," said Pearl Mouth.

Ciad asked her what that chance was, and she told him that if he would find Mountain of Fierceness, the son of the King of Greece, and conquer him and bring back to her Blue Gold, she would get for him from her father what he wanted.

"Then," he said, "I will do what you say."

"Not so easily," said Pearl Mouth, "for no one in the world can overcome Mountain of Fierceness unless he has the *buaidh* (power of victory) of Soul of Steel, Prince of India."

"Then," said Ciad, "I will set off and find that."

Off he started and did not stop until he reached India. There he demanded *buaidh* from Soul of Steel.

"That I will not give you," said Soul of Steel.

Then Ciad said, "I will fight you for it."

"You will only throw away your life," said Soul of Steel, "for no man can conquer me but one."

"And who is that one?" said Ciad.

"The man who can kill the Giant of the Great Seas," said Soul of Steel.

"Then," said Ciad, "I'm that man," and he told his story to Soul of Steel.

Soul of Steel said Ciad was a wonderful hero entirely, and that he would gladly give him the *buaidh*.

"Take with you a branch," he said, "from the oak tree that grows before my castle, and it will give you *buaidh*."

Ciad went to the oak tree and off it broke a branch; but when it fell to the ground, it sprang up a great tree. And for every other branch he broke the same thing happened.

Soul of Steel came out and gave him his cloak. He said, "Spread this under." Ciad broke another branch, which fell on the cloak, and he carried it off, and went in search of Mountain of Fierceness.

He traveled away and away before him, over height, hill, and hollow, mountain, moor, and scrug, lone valley and great green glen, until at last and at length he found, in Africa, Mountain of Fierceness with all his men, gathered together on a hilltop. He walked up and asked what was happening.

They told him Mountain of Fierceness was being married to the Queen of the Indies. He pushed his way to where the priests were marrying them.

Mountain of Fierceness asked the stranger what he wanted.

Ciad said, "My errand is to meet and defeat you, Mountain of Fierceness."

"That, my good man, you cannot do," said Mountain of Fierceness. "In peace, return to your home, and in peace leave me, for I'm getting married."

"I'll never return until I've taken your life or made you grant me a request," said Ciad.

"I'll not give you my life, and I'll not grant you one request," said Mountain of Fierceness. "But I'll spit you on the point of my spear if you don't leave and go whence you came."

Then Ciad asked him to step out for a fight.

"I don't want to take your life or any man's life on this, my marriage-day," said Mountain of Fierceness. "So, I tell you that no man can overcome me unless he has *buaidh* from Soul of Steel, the Prince of India."

"And that I have," said Ciad, throwing the oak branch at his feet.

Mountain of Fierceness, astonished, looked at the branch, then said, "Will you spare my life?"

"On one condition," said Ciad, "and that is that you tell me where Blue Gold, Prince of Africa, whom you carried off from his bride a year ago, is, and how I may get him."

"Where he is and what he is, I can tell you," said Mountain of Fierceness, "but I very much doubt if ever you can get him. He is a wild pigeon in the Eastern Skies—and nothing can catch him but the magic net of the King of Ireland's Druid, a net that can only be purchased by one-third of the Riches of the World—and after that nothing can disenchant Blue Gold but nine grains of wheat that lie at the bottom of the Well of the World's End, which can not be emptied except by the labors of three thousand men in three thousand years."

When Ciad heard this he bade him goodbye. He sent Swift Sword to Ireland to get the loan of the magic net of the King of Ireland's Druid, on the promise of paying him one-third of the Riches of the World, and told Swift Sword to meet him with the net at the Well of the World's End.

Away and away then he traveled, over hills a hundred miles high, and valleys a hundred miles deep, across plains that living man had never crossed before, and through vast green woods so far from the world that the birds themselves never reached them, until at length and at last he reached the Well of the World's End. There he found Swift Sword before him, with the net of the King of Ireland's Druid.

With three blows of his blade Swift Sword blew dry the Well of the World's End, and they took from the bottom the nine grains of wheat. They spread the net in the Eastern Skies and caught in it a hundred thousand pigeons, amongst them one great wild pigeon, which was Blue Gold.

They fed to the pigeon the nine grains of wheat, and there stood up before them a handsome Prince—Blue Gold.

With him they traveled away and away, until they came to the Lake of the Singing Shore and to the little house where was

Pearl Mouth, who swooned from ecstasy at finding her Blue Gold again.

The four of them set out and traveled away and away, over mountains and valleys and great wide plains, until they came to the Castle of her father, the King of Persia, from whom she demanded the bottle of Ioca and the Riches of the World, for Ciad. And she told him what brave Ciad had accomplished.

The King of Persia said, "No man could ever take these two things from me, but I give them willingly to the brave champion, Ciad."

Ciad and Swift Sword spent that night in the King of Persia's castle, and in the morning set out for home. When they reached the Plain of the Dead, they shook one drop from the bottle of Ioca on Swift Sword's army, and all of them stood up alive.

Ciad then parted with Swift Sword, who went on to conquer the East. He, himself—for his time was now getting short—did not turn aside, but sped direct for home. And on the evening of the day on which the three years and a day would have expired, Ciad stood upon the spot on the seashore from which he had set out, and there found Dark Eye awaiting him.

He gave Dark Eye the bottle of Ioca, and her stepmother's spells were at once lifted. They journeyed to the island where he had left his brothers' bodies, Ceud and Mith-Ceud. On their bodies he shook a drop from the bottle of Ioca, and they were alive again. All of them now set out and sailed to Ciad's father's castle—he, Ceud, and Mith-Ceud and Dark Eye, with the bottle of Ioca and the Riches of the World.

A messenger was sent to France, to fetch its King to his daughter's marriage, and asking him to bring his sons and his great lords with him. Another messenger brought to the King of Ireland's Druid his magic net and a third of the Riches of the World, and invited the King of Ireland and all his Court to the marriage. A hundred Kings sat down to the wedding feast. The feasting lasted ninety-nine days and ninety-nine nights, and the last day and night were better than the first.

Ciad and Dark Eye lived a long life and a happy one. And may you and I do the same.

THE KNIGHT OF THE
GLEN'S STEED O' BELLS

ONCE upon a time there was a King and Queen of Ireland who had three brave sons. The Queen died and the King married again. Their stepmother was jealous of the three young Princes, and strove all she could to have them driven away. But the King, though he would humor her in all else, never would consent to part with the three brave lads who were the apple of his eye. No matter what she said, or did, or tried, she couldn't persuade him to gratify her deviltry.

Nearby the castle lived an old henwife to whom the Queen at length went, consulting her how to get rid of her stepsons. The henwife said she could contrive it if she was well enough paid.

"What payment do you ask?" says the Queen.

"Three things," says the old henwife, "As much meal as will make my breakfast, as much milk as will sup it, and as much wool as will stuff my ears."

The Queen easily agreed to that, and the henwife told her, "You will challenge the Princes to a game of chess, for *geasa* (Obligations that could not be refused without loss of honor). If they win they'll lay some trifling task on you—but if you win, you will lay *geasa* on them to steal for you the Knight of the Glen's Steed o' Bells, which three hundred champions have already tried to steal and lost their lives."

The Queen was pleased. To pay the hag, she asked how much meal would make her breakfast. "The grinding of seven times seven mills for seven years." How much milk would sup it? "The yield of the cows of seven hills for seven years." How much wool would stuff her ears? "The produce of the sheep of seven times seven plains for seven years." The Queen was astounded. But as she had bargained, she had to pay the hag her price.

That very night she invited her stepsons to play her each a game of chess. They agreed, and asked for what they should play.

"For *geasa*," says she.

Well and good. To the chessboard they sat, and she won from the two elder, but lost to the youngest. The elder boys asked to know their *geasa*, and she said, "You are to set off on the morrow and never come home till you bring to me the Knight of the Glen's Steed o' Bells."

The youngest was sad when he heard such dread *geasa* put upon his brothers. He said, "If my brothers must go on such murderous quest, I'll not stay behind. And," says he, "the *geasa* I leave upon you is that, till the day we return, if we ever do, you are to stand atop of the tallest tower of our father's castle with your face to the wind, your food and your drink—a sheaf of corn and a tub of water."

And when, next morn, the brave boys had set off on their sad journey, from a distance turned for a last look, they saw the evil woman starting her penance on the castle's topmost tower.

Three days and three nights the young Princes traveled, and on the fourth, at noon, met a tall dark man on horseback, who inquired whither they went and what their errand.

"Well, well, well!!" says he, shaking his head in sadness. "Heart-sorry I am for ye. Are ye aware," says he, "brave boys, that three hundred of Ireland's choicest champions have tried that feat before, and every one of them lost his life?" They said they knew it, but go they must—and told him their story.

Says he, "I'm the famed Black Thief of Sloan; twice I have tried to steal the Steed o' Bells, and the most my cleverness got me was to escape with the life. The Knight of the Glen has twenty armed men guarding his Steed o' Bells by day and twenty by night. Every time that anyone but his master lays hands upon the Steed, hung with a hundred bells, he shakes himself and the alarm is heard over half of Ireland. Then to be boiled in oil is the doom of the reckless thief."

"'Tis hard," they said, "but harder would be the losing of our honor. The worst that can befall us is loss of our lives, and we're ready for that."

"You're brave, bold fellows," says the Thief, "and have my admiration. And as you're resolved on defying danger and death, I'm with you. I'll aid you all aid that I can, and at the worst lose my life along with you."

They thanked the Black Thief, and all four set forth. They journeyed far and very far, till late one evening they reached by the castle of the Knight of the Glen.

The Black Thief of Sloan said the luck was with them—for there was a great feast proceeding in the castle, gorging and drinking and carousing. The castle's carousing made easy the Black Thief's stealing a keg of wine and rolling it in among the stable guards, who fell to drinking, and ere midnight were all stretched asleep.

"Now is our chance, if we have any," says the Black Thief.

Then into the stable with them. But the moment they laid hands on the Steed, he shook himself and, far and wide, alarmed the world.

The Knight of the Glen, aroused, commanded all hands to rush to the stables, for his Steed was a-stealing!

The Black Thief, well aware this would happen, hid himself and the three lads on the hayloft; and after the company invaded and searched the stables, they went back and reported that the Steed had given a false alarm.

"That's odd," says the Knight, and they resumed their carousing.

Again, then, the Black Thief laid hands on the Steed, and again he shook his bells, alarming louder than before. The Knight ordered all hands to dash for the stables, where there surely was a thief trying to steal the Steed. The Thief had well hid himself and the boys again, so that the men returned to the Knight with report that the shaking of the bells was an accident only.

A third time the Thief caused the Steed to sound the alarm. For it was his plan to feed the revelers with false alarms, till they'd cease giving heed. But the Knight this time said, "There's most certainly a thief in the stable! I'll have to go with you and make search myself."

And the Knight searched so thoroughly that, lo and behold, he discovered them all four! He had them marched into the Castle Hall, and a great caldron brought in, filled with oil, and put upon the fire.

He said to the Black Thief, "Twice before you've attempted to steal my Steed and escaped—the only man who ever did. This third try is the finish of you. How does it feel," says he, taunting, "to be shaking hands with Death?"

The Black Thief scouted it. Says he, "I've been nearer Death before and cheated him. Maybe I'll deceive him this time, too."

"Not likely!" crowed the Knight. "Moreover, you never *could* have been as near death as you are now."

"I was, and I can prove it," says the Black Thief.

Says the Knight, "Before you go in the caldron, you might try to prove to me what I can't believe."

"I will do that," says the Black Thief, "on one condition—that you pardon the youngest of these Princes, if I convince you."

"I'll easily agree to that," says the Knight, "because the proving is impossible."

"Good!" says the Black Thief. "Then hear to my story, all of ye."

"There was once," says he, "when I set out to rob the castle of the Lord of Lagan. Reaching there in middle of the night, when all should be sleeping, I found it lit up and the place in wild furor. A band of robbers had got ahead of me, plundered the place, and fled! Now servants and soldiers were scouring the country to find them. In a fright I took to my heels and didn't stop running for nine miles. I drew on a house with blazing fire lit in it, but nobody without or within. Entering in, I was warming myself by the fire when I heard the tramp of people coming to the door. I said to me, 'Here's the pursuers—and I'm captured!'

"Up I jumped, climbed to the half-loft overhead, and lay down among goat skins and horses' harness piled there—and lay peering down. In of the door comes four men, hauling bags with them—empties heaps of gold and silver on the table and begins to count the swag. They were laughing loud and hearty, saying how well they had outwitted that damned rascal, the Black Thief of Sloan, who, they had heard, had planned to rob the castle that very night. 'Ha! Ha! Ha! Ha! Won't the black ruffian be sore bitten!' They said I had been too long robbing the country, giving other, honest, robbers no chance to live. They talked of how they, with all other robbers, conspired now to end my life, and went over all the tortures they'd put me to, before butchering me outright.

"As ill luck would have it, I was that instant overcome by a mighty sneeze! The four villains jumped to their feet and drew their knives. 'There's some renegade spying on us!' they shouted. 'Get him down till we rip his black heart out!'

"Myself was stretched on a loose plank at the loft's edge, where I had crept out, the better to watch and listen—protected by a goat skin over me. I took a terrible fit of trembling—trembled and shivered and shook so that the plank gave way, and down to their midst I came tumbling, an object black-faced, a goat-skin around him, horns crowning his head, and harness chains banging around him!

" 'The devil! the devil! the devil!' they cried. 'He's got us at last!' Yelling and screeching, they fled, one of them through the front door, another by the back door, and a pair went through the window!—Leaving myself in possession of all the plunder!

"Don't you think," says the Black Thief to the Knight of the

Glen, "that I was as near death then as I am now—and escaped?"

Says the Knight of the Glen, "You certainly were! I'm astounded! You have well won this young Prince's life. He's freed."

"For all that," says the Black Thief, "there was another time when death was as near me as either then or now."

"That would be an amazing thing," says the Knight. "Will you consent to leave the account of it with us before you go in the caldron?"

"I will," says the Black Thief, "on condition that if I make good my word—you pardon the second young Prince."

"Upon my honor, I'll agree," says the Knight.

"All right, then," says the Black Thief. "Well," says he, "there were, one time, three witches in Scotland who were known to all the world's robbers for possessing vast wealth. The most notable of the world's robbers had tried to rob them and lost their lives, for they never let their bags of gold out of hand all day, and put them for pillows at night. Then I, reckless, boasted that I'd rob them.

"I set out to Scotland, came to their place, and slipped in the house in middle of the night, when they were snoring. I had with me three bags of shingles. Under the head of each hag, I edged a bag of shingles as I worked out a bag of gold. To my joy, I had three bags of gold, leaving the door,—and laughing to myself at the peaceful snoring of the three hussies. But lo, didn't the door bang to waken a graveyard! Next minute I was flying over the hills, with the three witches in shape of three hounds in pursuit. I dropped the bags and sped for all I was worth. Fast and fast as I ran, the dogs were gaining on me at every bound—till they came so close that their hot breath blew on my neck. Then up a tree with me—which I knew dogs couldn't climb.

"One turned herself into a hatchet and one to a saw—and both began chopping and sawing the tree at the bottom. The third, taking her own shape, stood by watching for the tree to fall, that she might tear me limb from limb. The hatchet and the saw, each from its own side, were working faster and faster, now near meeting. The tree and myself began trembling, tottering, and the heart was leaving my mouth—when the cock crew for break of day—and the foul hags vanished!

"And what do you think of that for a narrow escape?" says the Black Thief.

"I think," says the Knight, who was panting for breath—"I think," says he, "you have worthily earned your second friend's life. He has a full and free pardon."

Says the Black Thief of Sloan, "Still, those escapes were nothing, beside another escape I had—a real one!"

Says the Knight of the Glen, "You couldn't have had more wonderful."

"I'll prove it to you," says the Black Thief, "if you pardon the third lad."

"Agreed," says the Knight of the Glen. "I wasn't overkeen on having the lives of these boys anyhow. 'Tis yourself only that I'm most wishful to annihilate—for while you live I'm never sure my Steed's safe."

"Thanky indeed for the compliment," says the Black Thief. "Well, here's your story for you:

"There was once, when I was off on a roving expedition and traveling through wild and rocky mountains, I stumbled over a *spink* (cliff) one evening and fell and rolled, and rolled and fell, till I struck the bottom of a narrow gorge far below. And what did I land beside, but a terrifying Giant cooking his supper. 'I'm glad you've come,' says he, 'for I hadn't as much meat as would take the edge off my appetite.'

"He reached for me, but I grabbed hold of a spit whose point was reddened in the fire, and rammed his two eyes out. He roared so that I thought the rocks would sunder, and cried, 'I'll give you the most beautiful death man or mortal ever got in this world!' He couldn't, of course, see anything, but he sprang toward me with arms outspread, and the gorge was so narrow that there was no chance of passing him without his enfolding me. So I backed away and away up the gorge ahead of his advance, till I reached where the gorge ended against cliffs no man could climb; but fortunately there was a cave, within which I darted—

a cave filled with goats, there gathered for the night. If he pursued me here, I could easily escape him among the goats and get out. But he was too wise! He seated himself in the cave's mouth, swearing he would never leave the spot till I'd either come out or die within of hunger. And there he was till morning!

"In the morning he called on his goats to come out. As they started past him, one by one, he'd embrace each one as it passed, and croon to it, 'Oh, my dear, dear goat, you can see me, your fond master, but I can't see you since that scoundrel within put my eyes out.'

"A great buck-goat in the cave, I quick got hold of, and cut his throat—then skinned him, got into the skin, and on all fours took my place in the line passing him. When I would creep by him, the old rascal embraced me, crooning, 'Oh, my dear, dear old buck, you can see me, your fond master, but I can't see you since that scoundrel within put my eyes out.' I trembled so with terror and shook so with mirth, both at once, that the heart was leaving my mouth while his arms were still round me. But Heaven saved me, for, putting a kiss on my nose, he passed me on.

"And now, don't you think, Knight," says he, "that that was as close call for life as you ever heard tell of?"

"I'll surely grant that," says the Knight. "And you've well won his life for the third of these boys. And now," says he, "I'm sorry, but it's into the caldron with yourself, and get your agony over with."

Says the Black Thief, "If I can prove to you that I was still another time nearer my end than at any those, will you let me go with my friends?"

"I will not!" says the Knight. "On no account can your life be spared. You die this night—will never see tomorrow's sun. But I'm so eager to hear how any man could possibly be nearer death than that last time, that I'll spare your life for one half hour, till we've heard your story."

"Even so," says the Black Thief, "the story you'll have. Once when I was returning through the same country where I had the encounter I've narrated, I came late to a castle, and went in to ask lodging for the night. I found a girl sitting at the kitchen fire with a baby on her knee, and she crying and wailing piteously.

"Says I, 'My good girl, what's the matter?' And she told me.

" 'In this castle,' she says, 'there lives a fearful Giant who is blind because his eyes were put out for his badness. He's compelled me to his service and makes me do whatsoever he bids. Here,' says she, 'is a little child that he stole and brought me last night; and when he was leaving this morning, he commanded me to have it cooked for his supper when he'd return.' Says she, 'I can't do it and I won't ever do it, and when he comes home my own life will be ended!'

"I said, 'Never mind. I'll fix that.'

"I went to the yard, killed a little pig, came back, and cutting off the left-hand little finger of the child, put it in the pot with the pig, for cooking. I said 'When the fellow comes home, serve him that dish for supper; and if he raises any doubts about the dish, fish up and hand him the baby's finger.'

"Of a sudden, didn't we hear, unexpected come in, the Giant roaring for his supper!

"I ran in a small room off the kitchen, which I found filled with naked corpses. I whisked off my clothes and lay down among them.

"The fellow wasn't long eating till he got up in a thundering rage, crying this wasn't a baby's flesh he was eating. The girl put his own hand in the dish and had him lift the baby's finger— which contented him, and he finished the meal. But then he said he hadn't had half enough meat and must cut him a steak off his stock of corpses!

"With a great carving knife, into the room he slipped, and began feeling the bodies. 'This one,' he said, 'is too tough,' and 'this fellow's too thin,' and 'this lad hasn't a bit on his bones at all' —casting them aside, one after another. Till he reached myself. He grasped me here and there and finally said, 'Ha! This buck is just right!'

"He lifted his knife and took a slice off my thigh, whilst I gritted my teeth and held in the screeches that were bursting to get out.

"He finished his supper on me, and then stretched himself to sleep—where, do you think, but right across the room door! I had to get out! I arose and overleaped him—but as I did, I touched the ruffian in my leap and aroused him.

"Away with me! And away with him after the sound of my footfalls! Yet, no sooner were we out of doors where he wouldn't easy hear me, but he snatched from his finger a magic ring he wore, and flung it after me, saying 'Ring, ring, hold fast.' And on the big toe of my right foot the ring settled itself! He'd then call, 'Ring, ring, where are you?' And the ring would answer, 'Master, master, I am here.'

"The fellow was as speedy as myself, if not speedier. I twisted and turned, ran up and down, leaped this way and that, trying every trick in my corpus—but all to no good, for still he'd cry, 'Ring, ring, where are you?' and still it would answer, 'Master, master, here I am.' Till at long and at last, I got exhausted and was ready to give in, when coming to a deep black pool, Heaven put it in my heart to whip off, with my knife, the ringed toe and cast it in the pool's center. And now when the ruffian called, 'Ring, ring, where are you?' and that ring answered from deep, deep, 'Master, master, I am here,'—into the pool the madman dashed—sank—and was never more heard of."

"Wonderful! Wonderful! Delightful and astounding!" cries the Knight of the Glen. "And 'tis pity," says he, "that such a rare narrator must die. But die, alas, he must and will. And that this sad minute—into the caldron with you."

"He won't go in the caldron—now or ever," cries a withered old woman who had been sitting by, in silence and unnoticed. She was the Knight's old nurse.

"What do you mean?" demands the Knight.

"I mean," says she, coming forward boldly, "that that good, brave man isn't going to die—tonight or tomorrow night, or any day or night—till his time comes!"

The Knight stood, dumfounded. Everyone was astounded. Says she to the Knight, "Let everyone here see your left hand." She lifted the hand without waiting—and behold, that hand's little finger was gone!

Says she, "All my life long, I've been trying to discover the brave man who saved your life when you were a condemned baby on my knee. Thank the Lord, there he now stands."

All of the company were thunderstruck! The Knight of the Glen was dazed! When he got his senses and speeches, he threw his arms around the Black Thief and near smothered him. "My gallant, noble saviour," says he, "I'll not insult you, saying your life is yours—but *my* life is yours!—I'm yours—this castle and all's in it are yours. Here you'll stay your life's remainder, co-equal, co-master with me—besides, for your noble sake, on these three noble young Princes of Ireland, I freely bestow my Steed o' Bells."

The Knight of the Glen, the Black Thief, and friends accompanied the brave boys well on their way, the Steed with them. They thanked the Knight, and they told the Black Thief they could never enough thank him.

They traveled fast and far, nights and days, till at last, they came in sight of their father's castle—on topmost tower of which they saw standing their cruel stepmother—with her face to the wind, watching for them that she never expected to see! When she did now see them, returning in triumph, the wonderful Steed o' Bells with them, she put from her a cry that rang three times around Ireland, and dashed herself from her perch to destruction!

Mightily rejoiced was their father, the King, to see them and embrace them. He divided on them his kingdom. They were crowned with great joy. Within a year they wedded the three most beautiful of Europe's Princesses.

In the wide world there were no three happier pairs. And if they were happy then, in all their long lives after they knew no day less happy.

May a like fate be yours and mine.

THE WEE RED MAN

'Twas in the faraway of long ago, when the world was rarer and happenings queerer, a thousand times, than they are today, that it befell.

And 'twas in Donegal—where fought and wrought against Fate and the Devil, Donal O'Donnell, a blacksmith by trade, and as kindly a creature as dog ever barked at. After a wrestle and tussle with the world and his wife, both got the better of him and left him as poor as a miresnipe on March's first day. There came a morning, at last, that he got out of bed without the making of a meal in the house.

Donal walked mournful from his cottage and stood in the door of his blacksmith's forge adjoining, his shoulder leant against the jamb, arms crossed, eyes downcast, and heart sad. At once he heard clatter of a horse, and lifting his eyes, beheld riding up the road, a Little Red Man upon a little pony.

The Little Red Man drew up at the forge-door with a "God save ye, Donal O'Donnell."

"Save yourself," says Donal. "Is it anything I can do for you?"

"Would you kindly lend me," says the Little Red Man, "the loan of your forge-fire for a few minutes till I shoe my horse?"

"With a heart and a half," says Donal O'Donnell, who was always the heart and soul of a good fellow.

"And would you lend me," says the Little Red Man, "the loan of a carving knife?"

Now Donal in all his born days had never before heard of a horse being shod with a carving knife, but he was too polite to question a stranger. So a carving knife he fetched him; and on a big stone that stood by the forge-door, the Little Red Man sharpened the carving knife—sharpened it up, sharpened it up, and sharpened it up till he could finger its edge only genteely. Then proceeding to his pony, he cut the four legs off him at the knee, gathered them in his arms, stuck them into the forge-fire, and covered them up with coals.

"Donal O'Donnell," says the Little Red Fellow, "would you kindly blow the bellows for me?"

Now Donal was dumfounded at this new way of shoeing a horse, but he was too polite to question a stranger; so he took hold of the bellows and blew them up, till at length he thought the legs must be consumed to a cinder. Then the Little Red Fellow says, "I think they're done now."

Going over to the fire and raking the coals aside, the Little Fellow lifts out—lo and behold! four new legs with a new set of shoes at the end of them—goes out and sticks the four legs under the pony! Jumping on the pony's back then, he says, "Good morning to ye, thank ye, and good luck to ye, Donal O'Donnell," and rides off with him.

Donal, all dumfounded, stood in his forge-door, looking after the Little Red Fellow; and when the senses and speeches returned to him, he said, "Well, that's the wonderfullest way, and the convenientest, that I ever heard tell of shoeing a horse! It's wish I do that I had known that method thirty years ago—'tis the rich man I'd be now."

The words weren't well out of Donal's mouth when he heard

the clatter of a horse again, and looking down the road, whom should he see coming riding but the King of Ireland, himself, mounted upon a beautiful, big, black, dancing, prancing charger.

When the King of Ireland came as far as the forge, he reined in his beautiful, big, black, dancing, prancing charger and says, "God save ye, Donal O'Donnell!"

"God save yourself, King of Ireland," says Donal. "Is it anything I can do for ye?"

"Ye can shoe my beautiful charger for me," says the King of Ireland, jumping off and throwing the reins to Donal. "Whilst you're shoeing him," says the King of Ireland, "I'll take a dander up the hill here and look around upon my kingdom. Take good care of my steed," says he, "because he's the valuablest in Ireland or out of it."

"The best of care he'll encounter with me," says Donal, leading the steed into the forge as the King went strolling up the hill.

Donal, he then got hold of his carving knife—for to try the new way of shoeing a horse. Upon the big stone by the forge-door he sharpened up the carving knife, sharpened it up and sharpened it up, till he had a fine edge on it, then proceeding to the King of Ireland's beautiful, big, black, dancing, prancing charger, he cut the four legs off him at the knees, thrust them into the forge-fire, and covered them up with coals. Getting hold of the big bellows then, he blew them up, and blew them up and blew them up, and the flames came up and the flames came up— till at length, when he thought the legs must be done, he went to the fire and raked the coals aside. And behold ye, there wasn't anything there but cinders!

From the forge door he beheld the King of Ireland coming down the hill to get his horse—while there lay his beautiful, big, black, dancing, prancing steed, without a leg to him!

"Och, och!" says Donal, says he. "'Tis behead me the King of Ireland'll do for slaughtering his beautiful steed!" And jumping out of the back window, he ran for the woods.

When the King of Ireland entered the forge and beheld the spectacle that met his eyes, he flew in a red rage—home with him and turned out his soldiers to bring him Donal O'Donnell, dead or alive.

Three days and three nights the soldiers searched for Donal without finding him. On the fourth night, my poor Donal returned home and slept there. Early the next morning, he was up out of his bed, heavy-hearted. And wandering out of his house, stood in the door of his forge with arms crossed, shoulder lent against the door-jamb, and he gazing dejectedly at the ground. When all at once he heard the clatter of a horse coming up the road, and lifting his eye, what did he behold but the Wee Red Man again coming riding on his pony. But Donal saw that the Wee Red Fellow wasn't alone this morning: he had two others, one riding before him and one riding behind—two of the ugliest old hags that Donal had ever seen in his life before.

And when the Wee Red Fellow, between the two spectacles, drew up at the forge-door and hailed, "God save ye, Donal O'Donnell," gruff enough, Donal answered him, "Save yourself."

Then the Wee Red Man said, "Would you kindly lend me the loan of your forge-fire for a few minutes this morning?"

Donal, who was always the heart and soul of a good fellow, never could deny anything to anybody, so he answered, "Yes," shortly enough.

Then he stood aside to find what the Wee Red Fellow was up to this morning.

The lad jumped off his pony, and lifting in his arms the two ugly old hags, carried them into the forge, stuck them in the forge-fire, and covered them with coals. And, "Donal O'Donnell," says he, "would you kindly blow the bellows for me?"

Now Donal O'Donnell was dumfounded, but he was too polite to question a stranger. He took hold of the big bellows, and blew them up and blew them and blew them up—and the flames came up, and the flames came up, and the flames came up, till at length, when Donal considered that the old women must be burnt to a cinder, the Little Red Man says, "I think they're done, now."

And going to the fire and raking the coals aside, behold ye, the Little Red Fellow lifted out the beautifullest young maiden that Donal had ever beheld in all his born days—carried her out, seated her on the pony, jumped up behind, and saying, "Good morning, good luck to ye, and thank ye, Donal O'Donnell," he rode off.

All dumfounded, Donal stood in his forge-door, looking after the disappearing pair, and when his speeches came to him, he said, "That's the wonderfullest and the handiest way I ever heard tell of turning ugly old hags into beautiful young maidens. Now," says he, "I have an ugly old wife and an ugly old mother-in-law in the house here, and from cockcrow to candlelight the sorra a thing they do but jarring and jibing, squabbling and scolding—and when the two of them aren't scolding one another, both of them are scolding me. Now," says he, "wouldn't it be a grand thing entirely if I could get a beautiful young maiden out of the pair o' them."

Without any more ado, into the house he went, and there he saw his ugly old wife, at one side of the fire and his ugly old mother-in-law at the other side, jarring and squabbling and scolding, and both of them spitting at each other across the fire.

"By this and by that," says Donal, says he, stamping his foot on the floor, "I'll soon and sudden put an end to this music!"

Running at them he got hold of the pair in his arms and carried them out, screaming and yelling and howling and kicking—stuck the both of them into the forge-fire and covered them up with coals. Then to the big bellows he went, and blew them up and blew them up and blew them up—and the flames came up and the flames came up and the flames came up around the old women—till when at length Donal considered that they were done, he went to the fire, brushed the coals aside, and, lo and behold, the old women were burnt to two cinders in the fire!

Donal cried, "Now my life is lost, entirely. The King of Ireland'll behead me for killing his horse, and after that, they'll hang me for murdering my wife and my mother-in-law!"

Out of the forge with him, and away! He ran for three days and three nights without stopping, and on the fourth day, tired and hungry, sat down beside a stream of water and took out of his pocket the last bit of bread he had in the world.

Just then Donal heard a piteous voice at his elbow saying,

"Donal O'Donnell, I'm very hungry—Will you divide with me?" And looking around, whom should he see at his shoulder but the Wee Red Man!

Little as was the love that Donal owed the Little Red Man, the moment he saw the hungry look in the Little Fellow's eyes, he broke his bread in two and gave half of it to his enemy.

The Wee Red Fellow clapped his hands, saying, "Why, Donal O'Donnell, you're the best-hearted man in all the world, and I want to help you."

"Help me!" says Donal, says he, "Help me! You have helped me enough, and 'tis no more of your kind of help I'm hungering for. Begone with ye!"

"Oh, but Donal," says the Little Red Fellow, "I'm going to help you now in real earnest. Wherever you go I'll go with you as your servant-boy—and I promise we'll win fame and fortune."

But no, no, no! Donal would have none of him, even if he was paved all over with gold guineas. But the Little Red Fellow insisted and persisted so that Donal, at length, in order to get rid of him, had to let him come with him.

Off, then, they started. And at a point where the road was crossing a high hill, they saw a post standing up with a placard on it. And when they read it, what the placard said was that the King of France was dying, and all the greatest doctors in the world had tried to cure him, but failed. And the Queen of France was now offering five bags of gold to any doctor in the world who would cure the King.

The Little Red Man, he shouted for joy. "Now, Donal," says he, "your fortune is made!"

"What do you mean?" says Donal.

"It's go to France we'll do," says the Little Red Fellow, "and you'll cure the King and get five bags of gold."

"Is it me," says Donal, says he, "for to cure the King of France? I couldn't cure a calf, let alone cure a King."

"But," says the Little Red Man, "when I'm with you, Donal, there's nothing in the world you can't do."

And the Little Red Fellow wouldn't give Donal either ease or peace, but go. And he pushed Donal before him till they came to France and came to the King of France's castle. There the Wee Red Man knocked on the gates, and a soldier coming out asked them who they were, and what they wanted.

Says the Wee Red Man, says he, "This is my master, Donal O'Donnell, the most famous doctor in all Ireland, come here to cure your King."

When the soldier looked at the famous doctor in his greasy duds and smutty face, he took the flat of his sword and began walloping them away.

That instant wasn't a window thrown up in the castle, and who but the Queen of France, herself, should thrust out her head and call to the soldier, who was it he was driving away?

Says the soldier, "Two ragged imposters come from Ireland who pretend that one of them is a famous doctor come to cure the King."

"Don't drive them away! Don't drive them away!" says she. "When all the greatest doctors in the world have tried to cure him and have failed, these can't do worse than the greatest doctor of them all. Fetch them in," says she, "and let them have a try, anyhow."

The soldier had to lead the two of them into the castle and up to the King's bedchamber, where they saw the King lying dying, a sorry sight. All the greatest doctors in the world had tried their hand on him, and he was only worse after every doctor; and now he was given up and was dying entirely. The Queen and all the Court filled the room, crying over him, striving to keep up his heart while he was dying. The Queen, she ran toward them, and, says she, "Do you think you can cure my King for me?"

The Wee Red Man, stepping between her and Donal, said, "Yes, madam, my master, he thinks little about curing a dozen Kings afore breakfast-time of a morning."

She asked what necessities his master required for to help him cure the King, and the Wee Red Man said, first a pot of boiling water to be brought in and hung on the fire in the bedchamber—which was instantly done. Then he said his master was shy about curing Kings with people looking on; they must all leave the room. The Queen and all the Court trooped out, and the Little Red Man closed the door after them and turned the key in it.

When Donal found himself and the Little Red Fellow left alone with the dying King, he began to shake and to shiver, and "What-what-what is it you're up to now?" says Donal, says he.

Says the Little Red Man, "You just hold your tongue, and do as I tell ye. Look around ye," says he, "and get me a carving knife."

Donal, he threw up his hands in distraction and dread. "No, no, no!" says he. "No more of your carving knives for me. I got me fill o' them!"

But the Little Red Man commanded Donal, who had to obey. He had to search, and find, and carry to the Wee Red Man a carving knife that was dropping from his trembling fingers. The Little Red Man took it to the hearthstone, and sharpened up the carving knife, and sharpened it up and sharpened it up, till the edge of it could only be fingered genteely.

Then, while Donal looked on, shaking and shivering, and his knees knocking together, the Little Red Fellow went to the bed, took hold of the dying man by the hair of the head, and cut the head off the King, carried it over and put it in the pot of boiling water on the fire.

"Now, Donal," says he, "look about ye and get a stick and stir the King's head in the pot."

But Donal, who'd collapsed, cried, "No, no, no! I'll have no hand in this murder!"

"Hold your tongue," says the Little Red Man. "Get up and do as I tell ye!" And Donal, behold ye, had to get up, get hold of a stick, and begin stirring the King's head in the pot.

And as he stirred away and stirred away, the head melted away and melted away, till at length it melted away completely and disappeared in the pot.

And Donal, behold ye, had to get up, get hold of a stick, and begin stirring the King's head in the pot.

Then Donal collapsed again. "And now," says he—"now our lives are lost, anyhow!"

"Hold your tongue," says the Little Red Fellow, says he, "and get up and go on stirring the pot!"

And Donal had to rise up and begin again stirring the pot. And he hadn't been another many minutes stirring till he beheld a new little head beginning to come in the pot! And as he stirred away and stirred away, the head grew away and grew away, till at length it was the full size.

Then the Little Red Fellow, looking in the pot, said, "I think it's done now."

He lifted the head out of the pot, and stuck the head on the King in the bed. And that instant, the King sat up in bed, talking and chatting and laughing, completely cured, better than ever he'd ever been in all his born days before.

The Little Red Fellow opened the door and let in the Queen and the Court. And when she beheld the King sitting up in bed, talking and chatting and laughing, completely cured, the Queen, overjoyed, embraced and kissed the King. And with her arms wide, she then ran at Donal.

"No ma'am, thank you," says Donal, says he, checking her career. "I've a wife of me own at home."

On her bended knees she then fell and, with hands clasped, thanked Donal from the bottom of her heart. "You're surely," says she, "the most famous doctor the world ever knew. And," says she, "I'll give you your weight in gold every year if you remain and be the King's doctor for the remainder of your days."

Donal, who was trembling lest the King would take it in his mind to sneeze before the head was well stuck, he said, "No ma'am," says he. "The people at home in Ireland will be dying, and I must hurry home to cure them. Get me up my five bags of gold as quickly as you can."

The Queen had the five bags of gold brought up from the cellar; the Little Red Fellow got them on his back, and off for Ireland both of them started.

When they had traveled three days and three nights, the Little Red fellow looked down at his shoes, saw that they were badly worn, with his ten toes sticking out through them. And, "Donal," says he, "will you buy me a new pair of shoes?"

Now when Donal was a poor man, as you remember, he was the best-hearted man in all the world, would divide his last bit of bread with his enemy; but now that he was a rich man, his nature was completely altered. And he answered back, "No, the times are hard, money scarce, and I can't afford you any shoes. Go on and carry my gold home to Ireland."

The instant he showed himself a bad fellow, the Little Red Man, with the five bags of gold on his back, rose in the air and disappeared through the skies—leaving Donal on the road, alone and lonely, poorer than he had ever been in all his life before!

Donal's heart sank into his shoes, and he went stumbling along the road, wondering what he'd do, at all, at all. Next minute his hanging head struck against something, and behold ye, it was a post on the roadside! And there was a great placard on the post —which he began to read.

And what the placard said was that the King of Spain was dying, that all the greatest doctors in the world had tried to cure him, but failed, and the Queen of Spain was now offering ten bags of gold to any doctor in all the world who could cure the King.

For joy, Donal clapped his hands, and said, "Now my fortune's made! Now I know how to cure Kings!"

Off he started, running, and never stopped till he was in Spain and at the King's castle, rattling on the gate to get in.

When he answered the soldier who came out that he was the famous Irish doctor, Donal O'Donnell, come to cure the King, the soldier cried, "Yes, yes, we've heard of your fame! The Queen heard how you'd cured the King of France, and has been screening the earth's corners to find you! Come in, come in!"

He fetched Donal up to the King's bedchamber, where the Queen and all the Court filled the room; whilst the King, after being given up by all the greatest doctors, was dying, out and out.

When the soldier announced that here was the famous Irish doctor, Donal O'Donnell, come to cure the King, the Queen near fainted for joy. She threw herself on her knees to Donal and begged, "Oh, great Irish doctor, do you think you can cure my King for me?"

"Yes, ma'am," says Donal, says he, "I'll make short work of your man for you."

She asked him what he required to help cure the King. He wanted a pot of boiling water to be hung on the fire, and then all the people to leave the room. Both these things were soon done, and he locked the door behind them.

When he was alone with the dying King, the first thing he did was to get a carving knife. Stooping then to the hearthstone, he sharpened up the carving knife, and sharpened it up and sharpened it up, till he had a fine edge upon it. And next, taking the dying King by the hair o' the head, he cut the head off the King and dropped the head in the pot of boiling water. Getting a stick then, he began stirring the King's head in the pot. As he stirred away and stirred away, the head melted away and melted away, till at length the head completely disappeared in the pot.

"It's doing fine," says Donal, says he. "It's half done now."

He went on stirring away and watching away, and stirring away and watching away—but if he had been stirring away and watching away from that day to this day, Donal couldn't get any new head to come in the pot!

And after two hours of this, the Queen and the Court began beating on the door to get in. And there was the King of Spain, lying on the bed, without a head to him!

Donal, he collapsed on the floor, crying, "Now, my life is lost anyhow. And right well do I deserve it!"

At that instant wasn't there a tip-tap-tapping on the window. And whom should he see but the Little Red Man perched on the windowsill, wanting in.

In three shakes Donal had the window thrown up, and the Little Red Man hopped in and, snatching the stick from Donal's hand, began stirring the pot.

He hadn't given three stirs to the pot, when Donal looked in and saw a new little head begin to come in the pot! Three stirs more, and, behold ye, the head was the full size! The Little Red

Man looked in and said, "I think it's done now."

And taking the head from the pot, he went over and stuck the head on the King in the bed; and that instant the King sat up, chatting and talking and laughing, completely cured, better than ever he'd been in all of his born days! The Wee Red Fellow said, "Donal, I'll wait for you outside," and hopped out of the window.

Donal unlocked the door, and the Queen and the Court came in—to see the King sitting up, and talking and chatting and laughing, completely cured! The Queen, overcome with joy, embraced and kissed the King, then fell on her knees before Donal, thanking him from the bottom of her heart and offering him three times his weight in gold, as a salary every year, if he'd remain and be the King's doctor for the remainder of his life.

But Donal all nervous, answered, "No ma'am. The people in Ireland will be dying, and I must hurry home to cure them—Get me up my ten bags of gold, as quickly as you can." Which she did.

Donal carried the bags out, loaded them on the Little Fellow's back, and off they started for Ireland. Three days and three nights they traveled before them, and on the fourth day the Little Red Man, looking down at his shoes, saw they were badly worn, with his ten toes sticking out through them, and he said, "Donal, buy me a new pair of shoes."

Says Donal, says he, "Go buy yourself a hundred thousand pairs of shoes. The money is yours, not mine. It is you that earned it, and it is you that has the right to spend it for whatsoever you please."

"Why Donal," says the Wee Red Man, "you are back again your own good-hearted self! Now," says he, "I want no shoes from you. I want none of your gold. I want nothing, for I'm one of the Gentle People, the Fairies, and anything in the world I want, I've only to wish for and I'll have it. I only asked the shoes of you to test you. Now that you're your own good-hearted self again, the gold will be yours, all yours, and nobody but yours— and I'll carry it home for you to Ireland."

Off they started, and never stopped, halted, nor paused till they reached Ireland and reached the top of the hill above Donal's own house, where they could see Donal's house and forge in the valley below.

There the Little Red Man laid down the ten bags of gold at Donal's feet and said, "Now, Donal, you're the wealthiest man in all Ireland and should be the happiest. Good-bye, good luck to you, and God bless you!" And rising in the air, he disappeared through the skies.

Donal looked down at his ten bags of gold and said, "Now I'm the wealthiest man in all Ireland, and I'm the hap— hap— hap— Oh, no, no, no! I'm not happy! Sure the King of Ireland will behead me for killing his horse, and after that, they'll hang me for murdering my wife and my mother-in-law!—Sure," says he, "instead of being the happiest, it's the miserablest devil I am in all Ireland!"

A doleful eye he cast down to his home in the valley below. And there, behold ye, first thing he saw was the King of Ireland's beautiful, big, black dancing, prancing, steed, standing up outside his forge, with four new legs under him! And the next thing he beheld was his wife and his mother-in-law coming running out of the house to greet him!

With a joyful cry, he hoisted the ten bags of gold on his back and went galloping down the hillside.

And behold ye, when he met his wife and his mother-in-law, he found they were not only alive and well, but both of them had grown young, and both had grown beautiful—and what was better than all else besides, both of them were grown good-tempered once again!

Donal, all rejoiced, went home with his arms around them, and in his joy, he married his wife again. He bade all the world to the wedding. And that was the greatest wedding ever known before or since. It lasted nine days and nine nights, and the last day and night were better than the first. Donal built a castle with a window for every day in the year, where he and his wife, with his mother-in-law, lived happy and well, ever after.

QUEEN O' THE TINKERS

ONCE there was a King of Connacht, and a great King he was—but a mighty bad one when anyone crossed him. He had one daughter, Fiona, the fame of whose beauty traveled far and was famed in all countries under the sun—a maiden, too, she was, as spirited as she was beautiful.

Now the King of all Ireland, at that time, happened in his old days to come visiting the King of Connacht, and was struck not only by Fiona's beauty, but also by the fact that she was as good as she was beautiful. Now, as he'd made up his mind to pass the kingship of all Ireland to his son, whilst himself should live in ease the remainder of his days, he had wished to see the Prince fitted with a wife who was qualified likewise to be Queen of Ireland; and since he had never met a better or more beautiful, or one more queenly than Fiona, he agreed with her father that the young couple should be married. To add, too, to the glory and grandeur of it, they planned the wedding to come off on the very day his son should be crowned—which great day was just five weeks away.

The King of Connacht, as you well may suppose, was dazed with delight for that his daughter should reign Queen over all Ireland; and next morn, in the presence of the King of Ireland and of his own Queen and of all the Court and all the lords and ladies, he had his daughter fetched in for the announcing of the great news. The King of Ireland himself got up from the throne where he was sitting, and addressing her said he'd singled her out for the wonderfullest honor that could befall any woman in this world—to marry his son, and with him rule over Ireland.

"Come forward, Fiona," says her overjoyed father, "and kiss the hand of the man who is bestowing on you the greatest honor the world knows."

Every soul there was as dumfounded as if a thunderbolt had fallen from heaven, when Fiona, drawing herself up, and eyes flashing, answered the two Kings:

"If you made me Queen of the World and Heaven besides, I wouldn't marry a man I don't love and never saw—I don't care if he was as exalted and as beautiful as one of our Lord's angels."

The breath of everyone in the Court stopped short.

"Do you, woman, know what you're saying?" demands her father, when his speeches came to him.

"I know well what I'm saying, your Royal Highness," says Fiona, "and all the Kings in the world couldn't make me say otherwise."

"Then, by this and by that, madam," says the King, her father, "you'll not live under my roof much longer. A week from this day," says he, addressing his commanders, "let every marriage-able man of noble blood who wants a matrimonial bargain, be mustered in the courtyard without. Whether she likes it or hates it, this girl will choose from among them a husband, and she'll depart with the chosen one—out of my sight forevermore."

The King of Ireland departed, sadly. But he left word that if, between now and the Prince's crowning Fiona should change her mind, he'd be a happy man.

Right enough, a week later, on a morning, all the nobles and knights and princes and kings, too, from far and near, were mustered in the King's courtyard, every one of them dressed in his best and looking his boldest and bravest, hoping he might have the luck to win the beautifullest girl in Ireland. All the people of all the countryside, too, for fifty miles every way, were there gathered—and all the streelers and strollers, *shulers* (tramps) and beggars as well—to view the spectacle and to witness Fiona's choosing.

Among the tribes assembled of vagrants and vagabonds was a gang of tinkers who came forward, impudently insisting that as their king, Jeremy Donn (the Brown-Haired), needed a wife, he, being of royal blood, must get his place in the ranks that Fiona was to choose from. The King of Connacht's commanders, naturally, were outraged by this brazenness, and dragged the whole gang before the King for sentencing.

"My sentence," says the King of Connacht, sternly, "is that their king is to take his stand with the rest of the other nobility that my daughter's to choose from." For it struck him as a God-sent chance to humiliate his disobedient daughter, out and out. So Jeremy Donn in his smutted face, tattered coat, and greasy breeches, planking his tools-budget at his feet, took his place in the ranks, to the great disgust and offense of all the noble candidates and to the dumfounding of the multitude. But withal, 'tis no harm to record that, spite of both dirt and rags, there wasn't among them—proud, conceited, handsome, grand ones though they were—a prouder, bolder, broad-shouldereder, handsomer man than Jeremy Donn, King of the Tinkers.

Fiona was brought out and seated on the platform, and all the nobles and knights and chiefs, princes and Kings marched past, she scanning them to the last man; and then, while the gathering sucked its breath, she stepped down, walked deliberate, and took her place beside Jeremy Donn.

"Jeremy Donn is my choice," she proclaimed. "There's no finer or handsomer or manlier man here this day—and no finer or manlier could the heart of me crave for."

And sure enough, for all his rags and grease, with his flashing brown eyes and curly red hair, he straight as an arrow, and broad-shouldered and lithe, the tinker, if he only had his manly face washed, was a picture for anyone to contemplate. Small wonder it was that Fiona's eyes flashed when they lighted on him.

As well you may suppose, all the crowd gasped and groaned at the thought of their King's daughter taking a tinker for her mate. And the princes and nobles and knights curled their lips and shook their heads and walked away in disgust—rejoiced, every man of them in his heart, that he escaped marrying a woman who must be madder than she was beautiful.

And the King, her father, when his right senses returned, spoke out and said, says he, "If you think this a joke, my damsel, 'tis the last bitter one you'll manufacture in my nearness. I hereby cut you off from all your inheritance with no more than the clothes on your back. I commit you, henceforth, to walk the world with your chosen tinkerman and carry his budget for him, wheresoever he wanders, between here and the World's End— Fare you well!"

While in pity and horror the crowd looked on, Fiona stooped and lifted the budget from the tinker's feet, over her silken-clad shoulder slung it, and, taking Jeremy Donn's hand in hers, and saying, "My chosen love, come!" strode off with him.

Asked Jeremy of his Princess, as they stepped out, "On what day was the new King of Ireland to marry you?"

"On the day he was to be crowned, one month from now," she answered.

"Between this and then," says Jeremy, says he, "you'll change your mind."

She looked up at him, her eyes wet, and said, "My choice is made and change I'll never do till either I die or the world ends."

Says Jeremy, "You know little of the hunger and hardships, ill luck and sore life of the tinkers."

"Walking the world with you," says Fiona, "neither hardship, hunger, nor hard luck will faze me, and I'll not know misery when I meet it."

Says Jeremy, "We'll not wed till the day set for the King's crowning, and your last chance of choosing him is passed. For right well I know your mind will change. Meantime," says he, "you'll be one of us and learn what our life's like."

The tribe was then traveling east. At finish of the first day, when Fiona shed her shoes, she beheld her delicate feet a sad sight of blisters.

"'Tis woeful work, traveling with tinkers," says Jeremy Donn.

"And I welcome the woe," says Fiona. "Every blister you witness is a joy, since I won it walking with you."

And when she cast Jeremy's budget from her shoulder the next night, 'twas sad striving to straighten the back that was bent all day under it. Says Jeremy Donn, says he, "'Tis woeful work, traveling with tinkers and bearing the King's budget, Fiona."

And she answered, "'Tis joyful work, Jeremy Donn, and wishing I am that I could walk to the world's end with you, bearing all burdens that life left on my King. My every ache would be a delight and every pang a pleasure."

On the third night, when they came to their journey's end, Fiona's silks were in tatters for the brambles and briars. Her soles were through her shoes, and she made a picture of misery.

"'Tis woeful work, traveling with tinkers, Fiona," says Jeremy Donn, "and worn and torn by the briars of the world."

"'Tis joyful, Jeremy," says she, "when one's company is the man her heart loves. If the world's briars tore in tatters the flesh o' me, every rip and rent would be a joy, remembering it was for my King I suffered."

On the night following, when they halted, Fiona tottered and dropped with weakness, for they hadn't had anything to eat all day.

"'Tis Purgatory painful, Fiona," says Jeremy Donn, "traveling with tinkers."

"'Tis nigh to Paradise, Jeremy," says Fiona, "and if I starved to death, 'twould be blissful dying for sake of Jeremy Donn."

Says Jeremy Donn, "You'll soon tire of both tinkers and tinkers' King, and long to be Queen of Ireland instead of Queen o' the Tinkers."

"Queen o' the Tinkers," she said, "with Jeremy Donn as my King, I'd not swap for Queen o' the World with Solomon, himself, as my mate."

The tinkers were eastwarding rapidly now, to the new King

of Ireland's crowning. For neither gathering, show, nor spectacle from end to wynd of Ireland, did they or one of their tribe ever miss. They came to a many-towered castle, the most gorgeous that Fiona had ever beheld. She asked, "What castle is this?" And they told her it was the specially-built palace and wedding present for her, whosoever should wed Ireland's new King.

"She'll need all grandeur that will help her to forget," says Fiona—"the poor girl who'll be made to marry a man she never knew and didn't love."

They traveled till they met a cavalcade of five hundred pack horses weighted with back burdens, five hundred pairs of carriage horses with carriages, coachmen, footmen, and grooms. And Fiona asked, "What and who are all these?"

They told her, "These are the horses and carriages with their fittings, and five hundred pack-loads of gold and silver, pearls, jewels, and valuables, intended for the fortunate one who'll wed the young King of Ireland."

"Heaven pity the poor woman!" says Fiona,—"as I pity her. She'll sore need all we witness—and more!"

They traveled till they met a great troop of five hundred pages in green and five hundred maidens in white. And says Fiona, "Who are all these, or where are they bound for?"

"These," they said, "are the pages and the maidens who'll wait on and serve the new King's Queen—for he has found a fair one willing and waiting to become his wife in case the King of Connacht's daughter, repenting her mistake, doesn't at the last minute change her mind and consent to marry him."

"Poor deluded fool, he!" says Fiona. "And poor deluded creature, she—the consenting one! All her pages and maidens, wealth, carriages, and castles couldn't buy her one hour of the joy I know with my poor tinkerman."

"Then, Fiona," says Jeremy Donn, "on the morrow's night, after we've seen the spectacle of the new King's crowning, we'll get wedded ourselves, if you're still of the same mind." Fiona just laughed at his doubting.

At last they came to the wonderful castle of the King of Ireland himself on the Hill of Tara—reached there the night before the next morning's wedding and crowning. Her own mother wouldn't know Fiona, so tattered was she, and torn, weather-beaten, wasted, and worn. There all the world was gathering against the great morrow and the spectacle of their lives, if they lived to be a hundred.

In the morn, before three thrones on a platform on the palace lawn, the crowds ranged themselves, with the impudent tinkers taking to themselves a brazen front place in the passionate ranks. When the hour of noon came, the old King with all his courtiers appeared and took places on the platform, the old King on one of the three thrones and his ministers around him. When he was seated his Trumpeter slipped to the front and on his trumpet blew three ringing blasts. When now he had all the world harkening, he in a great loud voice announced:

"Hereby we summon Fiona, the King of Connacht's daughter, if she be within hearing of our voice, to come forward and sit upon the left-hand throne and be wedded and crowned this day with the young King, and henceforth with him reign over our Kingdom of Ireland!"

Jeremy said in the ear of Fiona, who was on the ground pin-pricking the blisters that stung her feet, "Brave girl, there's your chance to quit a vagabond's life, its hunger and hardships, and take your shining place on Ireland's throne."

And answered him Fiona, "Ireland's throne could bring me nothing to equal the joy of sharing the hardships of Jeremy Donn."

The Trumpeter blew again three blasts and loudly cried: "Hereby a second time we summon Fiona, the King of Connacht's daughter, if she be within hearing of our voice, to come forward and sit upon the left-hand throne and be wedded and crowned this day with the young King, and henceforth with him reign over our Kingdom of Ireland!"

Jeremy nudged with his knee, Fiona, who with her pin was striving to remedy a great rent in her sorry garment—and said, "Dear girl, I implore you to take this chance to forsake misfortune and misery and sit a Queen on Ireland's throne."

And Fiona replied, "Misery and misfortune, with Jeremy

Donn to share them, are dearer far to me than the thrones of all the world without him."

The King's Trumpeter now blew a third time, and cried, "This is the third and last call for Fiona, the daughter of the King of Connacht, if she be within hearing of our voice, to come forward and take the left-hand throne, become the King of Ireland's wife, and Ireland's Queen forevermore!"

Jeremy Donn whispered to Fiona, who was endeavoring to get her teeth through a hard crust that a beggarman had shared with her—first food that day—"Fiona, dearest, I beseech you to bid good-bye to hunger and hardships, take your rightful seat on Ireland's throne, and be Ireland's glorious Queen from this hour till life's ending."

And replies Fiona, "Better to me this dry crust for my feasting, and be Queen o' the Tinkers with Jeremy Donn for my King, than Queen of all the thrones of all the world."

Said Jeremy Donn, "Do you mean that you're ready to be Queen o' the Tinkers, and my Queen, forevermore, to the giving-up of all the gold and all the glory, all delights and honors of the world?"

"Ready I am, Jeremy Donn," said she, "and the heart of me crying for you to take me and our tribe from here, and make me your wife and Queen, your people's Queen forevermore."

"Then, Love o' my Heart, put your hand in mine, till I make you my wife, adored and glorified Queen, before Heaven and the world."

She put her hand in Jeremy's. He raised her to her feet. Instantly all things swam to her closing eyes, her mind reeled, her heart throbbed! Then she ceased to know or feel anything excepting the joy that filled her soul as her tinker-lover led her off —led her where she didn't know, think or care!

She was brought to her sight and senses only by terrific huzzas that must shake both earth and sky! And gazing around, she found she was seated on a golden throne, and beside her on another throne, her Jeremy Donn! But the tinker's ragged coat had fallen from his shoulders, and in its place a shining satin garment, fringed with gold and silver, adorned his manly figure. And yes, a gorgeous silken garment covered herself from neck to ankle! A bishop in his robes was putting on her head, and on Jeremy's, golden crowns! Among the wildly cheering throng in front, she saw her late tinker companions slipping ragged cloaks from their shoulders and standing up in silks and velvets!

Her tinker-men and women were the lords and ladies of the land! And their Tinker-King, Jeremy Donn, was the Prince Royal of Ireland! He had tested her to make certain she could really love him ere he'd consent to take her for wife.

Now he was Ireland's King, and she its Queen. Thousands upon thousands were shouting in joy, "God bless the bravest King and the beautifullest Queen that Ireland ever knew or ever will know!"

Heavenly happy that day was Fiona. And a day less happy she didn't afterward know till her life's peaceful ending.

PRINCE FINN THE FAIR

ONCE upon a time, long, long ago, there were a King and a Queen in Ireland who had one son, Finn the Fair. The Queen died and the King married again; and the new Queen brought him another son. The new Queen loved her own son very much, and of Finn the Fair became jealous. But Finn, as he grew up, was such a lovely, brave, and manly fellow that he was the beloved of all the people—which made the Queen, his stepmother, dislike him still more and wish to get him out of the way of her own son, whom she hoped to see King of Ireland.

A great chess player was this Queen, without an equal in the land; and one day she bethought herself of a plan to get rid of Prince Finn. She challenged Finn to a game of chess, the winner to put *geasa*—or honor obligation—upon the other, and in Ireland then, no man of worth could shirk *geasa* laid upon him. The brave Finn would never refuse a challenge: he sat down and played his stepmother a game—and lost. Now Finn was great at hunting with hawk and hound, and the *geasa* the Queen laid on him was that on the next three days of his hunting, he should bring home to his father's castle the rarest prizes that ever were seen, or not come back himself. Prince Finn bowed and accepted the *geasa*.

Next morning, after breakfast, with his hound at his heels, his hawk on his hand, and he on his bright steed mounted, Prince Finn the Fair rode forth. He was pondering what rare prize in the world he could bring home that would be counted the rarest, when, riding down a sunny brae that led into the woods, he saw, sitting under a thornbush, a strange man, white-bearded, playing cards with himself, his right hand against his left.

"God save you, Prince Finn," the stranger greeted him.

"God save yourself, stranger," Prince Finn replied.

"Will you have a game of cards?" asked the stranger.

"I don't mind if I do," said Prince Finn.

"What will we play for?" asked the stranger.

"For whatever you say," said Finn.

Said the stranger, "I'm a wizard who can grant any man any wish, and I'd like to have my own wish, myself. Let it be that whoever wins the game can make a wish on the other, and get it."

"That suits me," said Prince Finn. "And anyway, I have a wish in my mind that's been worrying me."

"Well and good," said the wizard, and they began to play.

Prince Finn won. "And now, what's your wish?" asked the wizard.

Said Finn, "I have to please my stepmother with a very rare gift tonight. Now, in front of my father's castle is a three-hundred-acre lawn—and I wish that when I get home tonight the lawn may be crowded with ten thousand head of cattle, the rarest and finest that ever were in Ireland."

"You'll have your wish," said the wizard.

And behold, when Finn got home that night, the King and Queen and all the Court, and every soul in and around the Court, were out in wonder and astonishment viewing the grand lawn of the castle crowded with ten thousand head of the rarest and finest cattle ever seen in Ireland—which had suddenly appeared from no one knew where!

After breakfast next morning, his hound at his heels, his hawk on his hand, and he on his bright steed mounted, Prince Finn the Fair rode forth again. As he was descending a sunny brae that led to the woods, there, underneath a thornbush, he saw the wizard sitting, playing cards, his right hand against his left.

"God save you, Prince Finn," said the wizard.

"God save yourself," said Prince Finn.

"Will you play me a game of cards?" asked the wizard.

"I don't mind if I do," said Prince Finn. "For what will we play this morning?"

"Suppose we make the same wager again?" said the wizard.

"Agreed," said Prince Finn. And, dismounting, down he sat to the game. And he won again this morning.

"What is your wish?" said the wizard.

Said Prince Finn, "My father, the King, is very fond of the music of the woods—and I wish that when I return this evening, on every branch of every bush and tree on the lawn, there may be a rare songbird sitting and singing its sweetest and best, ten thousand of them."

"You have your wish," said the wizard.

And behold, when Finn rode home that evening, there wasn't a branch on bush or tree around the castle that didn't have on it a rare songbird—ten thousand of them, singing the sweetest and rarest that mortal ever heard. And out were the King and Queen, and every soul in and around the Court, lost in wonder and enchantment—and all the countryside, in wonder, was thronging to the castle, too.

Next morning, his hound at his heels, his hawk on his hand, and he on his bright steed mounted, Prince Finn the Fair rode forth once more. As he was riding down a sunny brae that led into the woods, there, under a thornbush, he again saw sitting the white-bearded stranger, playing cards, his right hand against his left.

"God save you, Prince Finn," said the stranger.

"God save yourself," said Prince Finn.

"How about a game of cards this morning, Prince Finn?"

"I don't mind," said Prince Finn. And he dismounted and sat down to the cards again—on the self-same terms as before.

But lo and behold you, this morning he lost!

"What is your wish, and what is my forfeit?" asked Prince Finn.

Said the other, "I'm the Wizard of the White Pine Wood. I live from here far and far and very far—out and away beyond the known world. In the last thousand years, many a brave champion has set out to find me and my castle; but of the thousands who set out only one ever reached there, and that man never returned to his world. To reach my kingdom and my castle, you have to climb the Crystal Mountains that only one man ever climbed; you have to cross the Flaming Desert that only one man ever crossed; you have to sail the Sea of Storms that only one man ever sailed; and then you have to find your impossible way through the Kingdom of Darkness. Within a year and a day from now, you are to find my kingdom, my castle, and me, or forfeit your life."

"It's a terrible task you've put before me," said Prince Finn.

"It is," said the wizard, "but they that play the game must pay the forfeit."

"I know it," said Prince Finn. "And the son of the King of Ireland never turns from any task, however terrible, that's put before him."

"Bravely spoken!" said the wizard. "And because you are so brave, and because I know that you dare not go home tonight without a rare gift, I will grant you for the last time whatsoever you wish."

Prince Finn thought for awhile, and then said, "I wish that my stepmother's head be now turned around, her face looking backward, and so remain for the year and a day of my trial."

"It's granted," said the wizard.

And sure enough, when Prince Finn reached home, he found all the castle in terrific commotion, the servants running hither

and thither, searching for doctors and magicians to try and rightify the Queen, whose head had been suddenly turned around on
her shoulders!

Prince Finn told his stepmother that she needn't worry herself,
or worry doctor or magician, for the Wizard of the White Pine
Wood had turned her head that way at his request; and so it
would remain, in spite of the world, for a year and a day, while
he was off on an impossible quest—which he described.

Worried though she was, the Queen rejoiced mightily when
she learnt his misfortune. And she said, "I expect and pray that
you'll never find the Wizard of the White Pine Wood, and so,
never return; but lest, by one chance in a million, you should, I
want to lay another *geasa* on you, which will kill your last hope
of ever coming back: I put it on you that in the year and a day
of your search for the wizard, you'll not only have to find him,
but find and win for your wife the fairest and most beautiful
maid in all the world. And failing to find and win her, never
return to this kingdom more."

Prince Finn heard his sentence without grumbling, reproving,
or repining.

Early next morning, after getting his father's blessing and
asking the blessing and protection of God on his quest, with his
hound at his heels, his hawk on his hand, and he on his bright
steed mounted, Prince Finn the Fair rode forth on his great
adventure.

He went by winding ways and waving woods and shimmering waters, up hills high-swelling, down hollows deep-dipping;
by vales and dales he rode, and over flower-decked plains to the
skies far-stretching. Dark nights came down on him and bright
morns rose over him, while he rode for far and far and very,
very far, till he thought that the world had no end. But at long
and at last one morning, he was astonished and dazzled by the
sight of a great shining, shimmering, burning light shooting from
the far distance ahead. When he neared it, he found that it was
the Crystal Mountains he had reached, dazzling great hills that
rose up and shut out the skies and the rest of the world!

Brave Prince Finn rode his steed against them, but on their icy, glassy, slippery, shimmering sides no foothold or toehold could his brave steed find. Then discarding the steed, he tried to climb them himself, but getting nor foothold nor handhold nor stranglehold, he fell down again and again, nigh breaking his bones—and rolled off them again. After doing his vain endeavor for hours till he was weary and worn, bruised, crushed, sick of heart, and nigh to Death's door, he mounted his poor bruised steed again and rode east and west, searching a shelter where he could lay down his aching head.

When night had fallen on him and he was about to give up the quest, he saw a light in the distance and drawing on it, found that it came from a little lone house in a wood. Entering in, he saw a very old man sitting by the fire, who said, "You're welcome, Prince Finn the Fair, the King of Ireland's son. Come sit to the fire and let go your weariness. While I'm getting ready a good supper for you, tell me, if you will, what brought you so far and very far from the world of human habitations."

And while the old man skinned and roasted a hare for supper, Prince Finn told him his story and what he was questing.

"I'm sorry for you, indeed, my brave fellow," said the old man. "I'm the Hermit of the Oak Wood. I have lived a hundred years in this end of the world, and I have seen and traveled most of the world, but never did I reach the Kingdom of the Wizard of the White Pine Wood. In my time I have seen a thousand of the world's greatest champions come this way on the same quest, but nine hundred and ninety of them turned back from here, defeated and despairing. The ten gallant ones who went on, I never saw or heard tell of again. Because I admire your courage, I ask you to stay here till you've rested and refreshed yourself, and then, I advise, turn your horse's head for home again."

"I thank you from my heart for your kindness," said Prince Finn, "but it would be a sad thing for the honor of Ireland, and ill become a King of Ireland's son, to let any danger daunt him or any obstacle turn him from his quest."

"'Tis well spoken," said the old man, "and only what I'd expect of a Prince of Ireland. And though I'd love to see you save your bright young life, I admire your choosing to dare danger and death; and what I can do to help you, I will."

After Prince Finn had for seven days rested and refreshed himself and his steed and his hound and his hawk, he was ready to pursue his journey, and would welcome any help the old man could give him.

The old man took from the chimney a whistle made of sycamore stem; from the doorstep he blew it, and in response, there came bounding to him a great lion, the Lion of Glen Dhu. The old man asked the lion to take Prince Finn over the Crystal Mountains.

"In the den that I left," said the Lion of Glen Dhu, "my young whelps are hungry, to my heart's pity, and I'll take your friend over the Crystal Mountains if he gives me his horse to feed my young ones."

"To part with the steed that I love," said Prince Finn, "is a thing I'll never do, though I should die today in my attempt to go farther."

"Then all four of you will die," said the Hermit, "for you never can cross those mountains alive. The King of Ireland's son mustn't waste life criminally."

Sad and sorrowful, Prince Finn at length had to give up his beloved steed—after he had thrown his arms around its neck, kissed it, and wept.

"Get on my back now," said the Lion of Glen Dhu. And after thanking the Hermit of the Oak Wood, Prince Finn, with his hound and his hawk, mounted the lion's back, and the lion faced the Crystal Mountains with all their peaks and all their glens and all their lochs of shining solid crystal made. The lion took a hill at a hop, a glen at a step, and a loch at a leap; and in short time had Finn and his friends safe on the other side, and told them goodbye.

With his hound at his heels and his hawk on his hand, but himself, alas, on no bright steed mounted, Prince Finn fared forward.

He went by winding ways and waving woods and shimmering

streams, up hills high-swelling, down hollows deep-dipping; by vales and dales he went, and flower-decked plains to the skies far-stretching. He went far farther than I could tell you, twice farther than you could tell me, and seven times farther than anyone else could tell the two of us—till at length, once when the bright day was going and the dark night was coming, he found himself on the edge of a burning, flaming, roaring desert, which, scotched and scorched and burning, bit him every time he dared approach. His hound howled, and his hawk screamed, and with him they cowered away from it. When he was weary and worn, approaching and fleeing, and the skin of him scorched and consumed in many places, he turned aside and walked eastward, seeking a place of shelter for the night.

He saw a light in the distance, and drawing on it found that it came from a little hut in the woods, where, on entering, he found a very, very old man sitting by the fire, who welcomed him, saying, "You're welcome, Prince Finn the Fair, the King of Ireland's son. Come to the fire and sit and let go your weariness. And tell me your story while I'm getting a bite of supper for you."

And when, roasting on the coals a hare for Finn's supper, the old man heard his story, he pitied him. He said, "Prince Finn, my brave fellow, I'm very sorry indeed for you. You have come upon a hopeless quest. I'm the lone Hermit of the Elm Wood— for two hundred years I have lived in the world and traveled to all known corners of it, and though I have heard tell of the Wizard of the White Pine Wood, never did I discover his kingdom or his castle. In the long years I have lived here, only ten of the world's greatest champions ever reached this far on the same vain search. Seven of them turned back from here; three went forward, but none ever returned. Be advised by me, don't waste your bright young life. Turn back while yet it is time."

Said Prince Finn, "I thank you from my heart for your kind concern, but it would be a sad thing for the honor of Ireland, and ill become a King of Ireland's son, to let any danger daunt him or any obstacle turn him from his quest. While the breath of life is in his bosom, always he must fare forward, till his goal is won or death, and death only, defeats him."

Said the old man, "'Tis bravely spoken, and well becoming a brave young prince, as you are, and the King of Ireland's son. Though I'm sorry for your determination, I admire your courage and will do all I can to help you. Eat a good supper, sleep well for the night, and tomorrow morning I'll see what I can do."

Prince Finn ate, and fed his hound and his hawk along with himself, and right soundly he slept. In the morning, after breakfast, the old man, taking down a whistle out of the chimney, blew it from the doorstep three times. In a short time, a great eagle came swooping through the skies and alighted in front of him—the Eagle of Slieve Cro.

The eagle asked, "Why have you called for me?"

The old man told him of Prince Finn and his quest, and asked that he should carry the King of Ireland's son across the burning desert.

"As you know," said the eagle, "I would do anything in the world for you, but that is something which, if I had my choice, I'd rather not do. However, my young ones on the cliffs of Caheer are mighty hungry. If Prince Finn will forfeit his hound to me for their feeding, I'll carry him over the Burning Desert."

"To give up for destruction the hound that I love," said Prince Finn, "is a thing that I'll never do."

And it was only after great and long argument from the old man, who showed him that if he didn't give up the hound it would be a vain throwing away of all their lives, that Finn, putting his arms around his hound's neck, kissed him, and dropping three tears upon him, resigned him.

With his hawk on his hand, he mounted the eagle's back, after heartily thanking the Hermit of the Elm Wood; and the eagle, then spreading his wings, soared to the skies, and high and high and very, very high above the Burning Desert, went winging. Yet, in spite of the height, many of the great bird's feathers were scorched, and withered, and burned; and the Eagle itself was scorched, as well as Prince Finn and his hawk. But at long and at last, they had passed the dreadful place. Prince Finn thanked and bade good-bye to the Eagle of Slieve Cro—and then, with his hawk on his hand, but no hound at his heels, and himself on no bright steed mounted, fared forth once more.

He went by winding ways and waving woods and shimmering waters, up hills high-swelling, and down hollows deep-dipping; by vales and dales he went, and over flower-decked plains to the skies far-stretching. He went far farther than I could tell you, twice farther than you could tell me, and ten times farther than anyone else could tell the two of us—for long and long and very, very long he journeyed—till once, when the bright day was going and the dark night was coming, he found himself approaching a rolling, roaring, crashing, frightening sea that rose and shrieked and swept in mountainous waves that licked and lashed the skies, as if it was the beginning of the destruction of the world and the coming of the Day of Doom.

After many times daring the approach to the sea, and being lashed and smashed and thrashed, reeled and rolled and turned and twisted by the hurricane that came off it, lifted off his legs and slammed to the earth, his breath stopped and his bones bruised, he at last realized that the man was not born or the boat built that could dare such a mad ocean.

Weary and worn, buffeted, bleeding, and torn, he turned aside at last, to seek shelter for the night. He saw a light in the distance, and drawing on it found that it came from a little hut in the woods, where, on entering, he found a very, very, very old man sitting by the fire, who welcomed him saying, "You're welcome, Prince Finn the Fair, the King of Ireland's son. Come to the fire and sit and let off your weariness. And tell me your story while I'm readying a bite for you to eat."

And when, roasting on the coals a hare for Finn's supper, the old man had heard his story, he pitied him. He said, "Prince Finn, my brave fellow, I'm sorry, very sorry indeed for you. You have come on a hopeless quest. I'm the Hermit of the Beech Wood, I have lived three hundred years in the world and gone to all ends of it. I have heard of the Wizard of the White Pine Wood, but never yet reached his kingdom, or discovered where he lives. In three hundred years only three of the world's most renowned champions ever penetrated this far. Two of them turned back from here, in despair, one went forward, but never returned. Be advised by me—don't waste your bright young life: turn back while it is time."

Said Prince Finn, "I thank you from my heart for your kind intentions, but it would be a sad thing for the honor of Ireland, and ill become a King of Ireland's son, to let any danger daunt him or any obstacle turn him from his quest. While the breath of life is in his bosom, always he must press onward till his goal is won, or death only, defeats him."

Said the old man, "It's bravely spoken, and well becoming a brave young prince as you are, and the King of Ireland's son. Though I regret your determination, I admire your courage and will do all I can to help you. Eat a good supper, sleep well for the night, and tomorrow morning I'll see what I can do to aid you."

Prince Finn fed his hawk and himself, and right soundly he slept. After he got up in the morning and had his breakfast, the old man, taking a whistle from the chimney, blew it from the doorstep. In short time Prince Finn beheld streaking toward them an otter the size of a calf. It was the Otter of Loch Bel Shiad.

"Why do you summon me this morning?" asked the otter.

The Hermit told of Prince Finn's request, and asked that it would carry the prince through the Sea of Storms.

"You know," said the otter, "I will do anything in the world for you, but that is one thing I would rather not do. Once in my life, and only once have I gone through that sea, and then I vowed never would I attempt the like again. However," he said, "my young pups in Loch Bel Shiad are hungry for their breakfast, and if the prince will let me have his hawk to feed them, I'll take him through the Sea of Storms or lose my life in the attempt."

"To part with the hawk that I love is a thing I won't do," said the prince.

But the old man argued with him, and persuaded him that it would be foolish to waste and throw away his bright young life, and made him consent against his will to part with his hawk— after he had fondled and stroked and kissed it, and over it dropped a tear.

Prince Finn thanked the Hermit of the Beech Wood heartily, and got on the otter's back. And the Otter of Loch Bel Shiad with him, plunged into the Sea of Storms.

They were whipped and lashed and buffeted and beaten, whisked on the waves' crests to the skies that came down to meet them, and dashed to the abysmal depths with the curling tops of the waves meeting in angry arches high and high overhead. When they were on top of a wild, dizzy wave, the Prince thought he never could descend again with his life in him. And when they were in the depths and he looked up, he felt sure he could never take his life out of this abyss. In all his career he had never dreamt of such an awful experience. But, after hours that seemed ages, behold! the wild waves began to go down and the waters to get smooth, till, on a sea that was like a pond in Paradise, so calm, so sweet and beautiful, they reached land.

"Now," said the Otter of Loch Bel Shiad, "three hours' travel from here begins the Kingdom of Impenetrable Darkness which man never has and never will penetrate by his own power. For three hundred miles extends this awful belt, to the very edge of the lawn of the castle of the Wizard of the White Pine Wood. There's no use your trying to get through it. Only three steps into it and you're lost forever—you can find your way neither backward nor forward nor eastward nor westward. And you'll never be seen nor heard of more. Don't try. Sit you down and rest on these green banks. Not long then, it will be till you see coming out of the skies three snow-white swans who will alight on the sea's marge. These three swans are the three daughters of the Wizard of the White Pine Wood. They come here each day to bathe. They are the three fairest, most beautiful maids in all the world, and the youngest, the smallest, Finola, is the fairest, most beautiful of all. By the edge of the sea, they'll shed their swan's skin and go in the waters. While they are bathing, do you take the crest of the smallest. Return to your place with it and wait for what will happen. If you do as you are directed, all may turn out well. Good-bye!" Then the Otter of Loch Bel Shiad dived into the sea and disappeared.

On a beautiful green bank on the margin of the sea, Prince Finn the Fair sat down to rest and recover himself and enjoy his liberation from the Sea of Storms. An hour he was sitting when he saw, coming out of the skies, three darling white swans that dipped down and alit on the sea's edge, some distance away.

There the swans' skins dropped off them, and three of the fairest maids eye ever beheld went into the waters. While they were disporting themselves, Prince Finn stole along and picked out the smallest of the three skins, took off its crest, and with it returned to his place of sitting.

When the maids came from the water and would don their skins again, behold the young one had no crest. Then it was that they saw Prince Finn, believed that he had taken it—and came begging it of him. At sight of Finola, whose face and head were now uncovered, the Prince was enchanted. Never in his life had he seen such beauty. And, indeed, when she looked on Prince Finn, she was just as much enchanted with him. He gave Finola her crest; he told them of his plight and his quest and the story of his long and sore journeying. Their hearts were filled with pity and sympathy, and admiration too, for him, and they said they would gladly do anything in the world to help him.

As they spoke night came down, and he must rest and sleep. They asked him to stretch on a flowery bed on the green bank, and they would rest by him, guard and shelter him for the night. Finola laid herself by his head, sheltering it all night with her wing. The two older lay, one by each side of him, meeting their wings across for his protection and warmth. Sweetly, peacefully, and refreshingly, he slept the night through; and when in the morning he had awakened, feeling a new man, they told him they would guide him through the Kingdom of Darkness which mortal man had never traversed before. Then they set out.

The great gloomy belt was thick-wooded with oak trees. Finola walked before, for him to follow, whilst the other two took to the tree tops, one on each side of the way he went. And behold, so dazzlingly white were the three swans that the reflection from their bodies created a twilight path along which he could, very slowly but surely, make his way, winding and twisting and ever following the fair one who lovingly led the way. For long and long, and far and far, they traveled so, guiding his steps by day, resting by him each night, and with their wings comforting and sheltering him, till, to his joy, he at last came out in a new bright world, with a dazzlingly grand castle rising on a hill at a short distance ahead. They were in the kingdom and at the castle of the Wizard of the White Pine Wood. And in the knowledge Prince Finn's heart leaped for joy. But, he said his joy would not be complete until he'd have fair Finola for wife.

Finola modestly replied that this would make her joy complete also.

The eldest maid said it would be difficult, if not impossible, to get their father's consent to this, because Finola he loved best of all, and out of his sight would seldom let her. "But," she said, "we'll do our best to help you—and to help sister Finola find her happiness."

They left Prince Finn to journey to the castle alone and present himself to their father while they winged off.

Of the year and a day which Prince Finn had been given to find the wizard, eleven months and eleven days had now passed, and the wizard, who had assured himself that Prince Finn would never find him, was astounded when the youth walked up to him, where he exercised his hounds on the lawn. Yet so high was the wizard's heart lifted by admiration of the boy's bravery that he offered him, "Look into my castle, and out of my castle, and around my castle, and the costliest gift you would wish to get and to take home to Erin with you, I'll not refuse."

Prince Finn at once answered him, "I have heard of the famed beauty of your youngest daughter, Finola, and the one gift that I ask is her hand in marriage."

The wizard was staggered. He stayed silent for a while. Then he said, "Such request I didn't dream of. With the heart in my bosom I would rather part than with Finola. But as I made a rash promise and that you have asked for one of my daughters, I'll keep the promise so far as to give you my eldest—though even that goes hard with me."

"That," said the Prince, "would be a great prize, indeed; but I am greedy and want a greater. I want Finola."

"I'm sorry," said the wizard. "Then I'll give you my second daughter."

"That, too," said Prince Finn, "would be a rare prize; but I want Finola."

The wizard was silent for awhile. Then he said: "Let me sleep on this, and in the morning I'll tell you what I'll do."

That night as Prince Finn was preparing to retire, there came a knock on his door, and the three beautiful sisters tiptoed in. They had come to tell him that their father would try to deceive him in the morning. He would pretend to be letting him choose from the three sisters, by leading him in the parlor and giving him to take for his wife the owner of either one of three hands thrust through a screen behind which the three sisters were supposed to be concealed—and his choice he would have to abide by. He must say no to all three—for they would be the hands of their three maids. Their father then would reluctantly have to place themselves behind the screen—and for better, for worse, Prince Finn would choose a hand and by his choice must abide.

"We'll pray that the hand you choose will be Finola's," they said.

"I trust to God that it will," he answered.

Next morning, after breakfast, the wizard took Prince Finn to the parlor, and showed him a screen by a door at the parlor's far end—a screen with three round holes in it.

"Behind that screen," he said, "are the three girls. At my order they'll thrust through it their left hands, and of the hands you will choose the one that will be the hand of your wife. And you must abide by your choice."

At the wizard's command, three left hands were thrust through the three holes in the screen, and Prince Finn, glancing at them, said, "I choose none of them. My wife is not there."

The wizard, angry, said, "You're hard to please! Now I'll give you your final choice." In a short time three other hands were thrust through the screen.

Prince Finn looked at them closely and intently. The three hands were alike as it was possible to be. But soon he noticed a slight tremble in one of the hands while the other two were steady. He seized the hand that trembled, pressed it, got an answering pressure, and said, "This is my wife."

When he let go the hand, Finola, her face beaming, stepped

from behind. Prince Finn embraced and kissed her. The Wizard, noting Finola's joy, showed him torn between grief and gladness. But he had to bestow them his blessing.

They were married. The Wizard bestowed on them his Magic Steed—and, on his back, off for Erin started the happy pair.

The Steed overtook the wind before, and the wind behind couldn't overtake him. His toes only touched the tops of the highest hills as he went, and the bits of sod, from his heels flying, were like a flock of swallows that followed. Old stars dipped behind the horizon aback of them, and new stars arose above the horizon ahead. The Kingdom of Darkness lightened and brightened as they swept through. The Sea of Storms subsided to let them swim over.

And lo, on the other side were waiting to greet them the Hermit of the Beech Wood and the Otter of Loch Bel Shiad. They had the hawk, alive and well, to put on Prince Finn's hand.

"Because you were such a brave fellow," said the Otter, "and loved your hawk so fondly, I couldn't sacrifice it, but kept it safe and well for you."

He thanked the Otter and said thanks and good-bye to the Hermit—and on they sped. The Burning Desert, as they approached it, took on the cool breath of Spring; and through it they found a flower-decked path between rows of green bushes, crowded with singing birds that made glad music as they went.

On the other side were waiting for them the Hermit of the Elm Wood and the Eagle of Slieve Cro with the hound, alive and well. They greeted them warmly.

Said the eagle, "Because you were such a brave fellow and loved your hound so fondly, I couldn't sacrifice him, but kept him sound and safe for you." He heartily thanked the Eagle and the Hermit and bade them good-bye.

Then, his hawk on his hand and his hound at his heels, Prince Finn and his bride fared forward. The Crystal Mountains, when they came to them, opened a flowery path all the way through. And, behold, at the other end, they found waiting for them the

Hermit of the Oak Wood and the Lion of Glen Dhu with Prince Finn's own brave bright steed!

Prince Finn was overjoyed as they greeted him. Said the lion, "Because you were such a brave fellow and so fondly loved your steed, I couldn't sacrifice him, but have kept him sound and well for you."

Prince Finn threw his arms around the steed's neck and kissed him. Then giving the Steed of Magic to his bride, he mounted his own. He thanked the Hermit and the Lion right heartily and bade them good-bye.

Like the wind, now, they went by winding ways and waving woods and shimmering streams, up hills high-swelling, down hollows deep-dipping; by vales and dales they rode, and flower-decked plains to the skies far-stretching.

At long and at last, they reached Ireland, and, soon, his father's castle. His bride by his side, his hawk on his hand, his hound at his heels, and he on his bright steed mounted, Prince Finn the Fair rode up. His stepmother, seeing them coming, gave a scream, threw up her hands, and fell dead. In joy, the King and all the court was out to meet them; and there was such rejoicing and feasting as had seldom ever been seen in Ireland before. They were wedded, and the King gave his throne to his son.

And Finn the Fair and Finola the Lovely lived and reigned happy and well from that glad day forward.

The Steed overtook the wind before, and the wind behind couldn't overtake him.

JACK AND
THE LORD HIGH MAYOR

ONCE on a time a poor woman living not a longways from
Dublin City had one son, Jack, a brave boy, merry as the mischief, and as full of roguery as an egg's full of meat. Jack was
mighty fond of all beasts, which he loved like brothers, and there
wasn't a wing in the wood which wasn't as familiar to him as his
pater-and-ave. He had a pet rabbit that made its bed on the cat's
back in the chimney corner; and when it wasn't using or abusing
the cat, the little animal would be following Jack's tail or his
mother's. The minute he tumbled out of bed in the morning,
Jack would hop to the door, and blow on a tin whistle—then the
birds of the wood, who were waiting, would wing their way to
him for their morning meal. He'd have around him a gathering
of them as great as Granuaile's army—they feeding and frolicking
with him.

Lo, and behold, there was a day that the Lord High Mayor of
Dublin with his royal staff of footmen and fine gentlemen were
passing that way, to visit the Prince of the North; and the Lord

High Mayor, getting a thirst on him by reason the day was desperately hot, dropped into Jack's mother's little house, and asked Jack, who was within, if he could have a bowl of buttermilk.

"You surely can, my Lord High Mayor," said Jack; "two, if you'll take them."

He raised a bit of a rod, gave the rabbit a tip of it, saying, "Rabbit, go look for my mother, and bring her here quick—to give the Lord High Mayor of Dublin a bowl of buttermilk."

The rabbit, after getting the switch, naturally ran out of the door. And Jack remarked, "My mother, she's gone to Galway, but the little vag will have her here in a jiffy."

This was just Jack's drollery, but the Lord High Mayor, not knowing the comical character he was, said, "But Galway is two hundred mile from here."

"No matter it was seven hundred," said the rogue. "There's many a bit o' magic trick that same little animal can work."

It wasn't two minutes till Jack's mother, who had been blading kale in the garden, strolled into the house, with the rabbit at her heels.

The Lord High Mayor was sent speechless with wonder. He said, "That's certainly the most wonderful animal that ever walked the world! He'd be beyond value to me, for there's often many a message I need sent quickly to the ends of Ireland. Will you sell him?"

"Oh!" said Jack, carrying on the game, "it would take a sweet penny to purchase such a hero."

"I'll gladly give a hundred pounds for the animal," said the Lord High Mayor.

Said Jack, "As I hate to deny the Lord High Mayor of Dublin any request that he'd ask, I'll let you have him for a hundred. I don't care if it does break my heart!"

The Lord High Mayor called on his treasurer to count out to Jack from his gold bag a hundred pounds—which he did. And, jumping with joy, and dancing with delight, he took up the rabbit and continued his journey.

When the Lord High Mayor, with his Court, reached the castle of the Prince of the North, he was bursting with desire to show the powers of his wonderful rabbit. And he said to the Prince, "I want you to do me a favor, by giving, tomorrow night, a great dinner in honor of my particular friend, the King of Munster." And he asked to have every lord and lady within a day's ride of the castle invited.

"But where's the King of Munster?" said the Prince, in surprise.

"He's where he ought to be," said the Lord High Mayor, "sitting on his golden throne at home, three hundred miles away."

"Is it crazy you are," said the Prince, "wanting me to give a dinner tomorrow night in honor of a man who is, at this minute, seven days' and seven nights' journey from here?"

"Ha! ha! ha!" laughed the Lord High Mayor, "That's the fun of the thing. I have discovered," said he, "a secret by which I can produce in five minutes any individual living within the earth's four corners. And I want to do you the honor of treating all your friends to the first sample of my secret."

"Well, that's extraordinary," said the Prince, "and I'm sure I'll be mightily honored."

Without delay the Prince began speeding messengers north, south, east, and west, inviting every lord and lady and man of high degree to a magnificent dinner to be given at his castle the very next night, in honor of Munster's King. And he had a hundred cooks sworn in to get up the greatest dinner that ever was contrived.

Very well and good. Next evening, the roads that reached the castle were black with lords and ladies and men of great degree who came driving and riding, walking, creeping, and crawling for the wonderful dinner. As the clock struck the dinner hour, every soul of them was in his seat, licking his lips. And they said, all together, "But where's the King o' Munster?"

The Prince proudly said, "My friend here, the Lord High Mayor of Dublin, will enlighten you about that."

"Where is he?" they said to the Lord High Mayor.

Said the Lord High Mayor, rising, "My dearly beloved friend, the King of Munster, is where he ought to be, sitting on his golden throne in his own parlor in Munster, seven days' and seven nights' journey from here. Dinner will begin the minute his Kingship arrives."

The instant they heard that, the lords and the ladies and men of great degree nearly raised the castle's roof with their riotous behavior. They shouted, "If the Lord High Mayor of Dublin conceits himself he can come to the North and play larks like this with the grandest people here, we'll teach him a lesson his tutor left out."

"Ha! ha! ha! ha!" laughed the Lord High Mayor, very hearty. "Keep your seats, gentlemen and ladies, and others, and sharpen your knives and forks, for the feast is soon going to begin."

Then he explained to them how he had got a wonderful secret by which he could produce within five minutes any man he needed, from the thither end of Patagonia or Peru, and that he was specially honoring his friend, the Prince, and all his good friends, the lords and ladies present and men of great degree, by giving first sample of the secret in their presence.

Right heartily he roared again at the row he had raised. And heartily they laughed when they drank it in. And they took their seats while the Lord High Mayor producing his rabbit and setting it on the floor, gave it its orders, tapped it behind with a *kippeen* [a twig] and sent it skipping from the room. Then he took his own seat at the Prince's right hand, and began sharpening his knife and fork. "For," said he, "gentlemen and ladies, the King of Munster will now be with you in two shakes of a lamb's lug."

Two minutes passed, and no King came. Three minutes, and no King. Five minutes went by, and no King yet. Said the Lord High Mayor, who was beginning to fidget a bit, "To be sure, Munster is a long way from here."

The head cook came in asking would he serve the turkeys, as they were beginning to burn. The Lord High Mayor flung three salt cellars at him, and told him to withdraw his ugly face for another two minutes.

Very well and good. The Prince himself at length began to grow uneasy. And the company were showing some concern when the rabbit was ten minutes gone, and neither King nor carle showing his nose yet.

"Look out o' the window," said the Lord High Mayor to the man who sat next it, "and tell me if you don't see the rabbit and the King coming up the avenue."

Ten men looked out of the window and reported that the only individual in the avenue was a strayed ass feeding on the flower beds.

"That's queer," says the Lord High Mayor.

"It is," says the Prince of the North.

"It most certainly is," growled the company.

Said the Lord High Mayor, "Gentlemen and ladies, have patience, for the King of Munster had maybe to get into his gold dress before leaving. I'll put my head on it, that he'll be here in two minutes more at most."

"Be careful with your head," muttered some ill-mannered guest.

The whole company began muttering, and the Prince getting mighty uneasy, when more minutes went by without a King coming. A crowd of cooks thronged into the room, tore off their aprons, and flung them at everyone's head that was handy, saying the dinner was burnt black as their shoe, and they'd have no further act or part in the ceremonies. The company then got cantankerous, and the Lord High Mayor of Dublin tried to calm them, saying, "Ladies, and gentlemen, I'm sorry, but it seems to me there's some mistake."

"And it seems to us," said they, "there's some danged mistake. Here we're in our hundreds, the cream of the country, from every art, part, and point of the compass, some of us feeling as if we'd fasted for a fortnight, and neither bit, scrap, nor particle to put in our mouths, because of a low-down prank that you thought you could play on us simple souls o' the North." And said they, "By this and by that, we'll take the worth of it out o' your corpus, and deliver you in Dublin with a mark on you every place ever your mother laid a thumb."

Upon the poor Lord High Mayor the party fell. And it was only by pitchforking dragoons into the room that the Prince was able to get the Lord High Mayor out of their fingers while a bit o' breath was left in his body.

But the lords and ladies didn't leave a whole pane in the castle windows, nor two sticks of furniture together, when they'd said their farewells.

It was a month's time before the Lord High Mayor of Dublin was fit to be fetched home. And as his party came nigh Dublin, he directed that they should halt at Jack's house, and his dragoons should seize the rascal and hang him to the first tree.

Whom should they see on the doorstep, as they came up, but my brave Jack, himself.

"There," said the Lord High Mayor, "is the unconsecrated vagabond. Give him no mercy."

But that minute, Jack, who wasn't watching the party and didn't see them, put his whistle to his mouth, and blew on it. The Lord High Mayor wondered what he was whistling for at this hour of the morning. But next instant he saw the skies darkening with the flocks of birds that gathered from the woods and the scrugs in answer to the usual call for the morning feed. They lit on Jack's head, hands, and shoulders, and made the size of a fair around about him.

The Lord High Mayor, amazed, restrained the dragoons and called to Jack, asking what kind of wonderful whistle was that he had; and if the birds always came at its call.

"Oh! my Lord High Mayor," said Jack, "this is an extraordinary whistle entirely. There isn't a bird in the world but must answer to it—come and alight, as you see these, all over and around you."

"Well! well! well!" said the Lord High Mayor. "That certainly is most extraordinary. Would you sell that little gadget?"

"Well," said Jack, "I'm no ways anxious to part with such a valuable object, but as I don't like to deny the Lord High Mayor of Dublin anything he covets, he can have it for only a hundred pounds."

"It's a bargain," said the Lord High Mayor. And he called upon his treasurer to pay a hundred golden pounds out of the money bag to Jack.

Then the Lord High Mayor, hugging the whistle, commanded the procession to make haste with him to Dublin. "Because," he said, "I want to surprise and astound all my city with this wonderful whistle, the like of which was never seen in the world before, and maybe never will again."

Very well and good. When the Lord High Mayor got home, he hired the biggest hall in Dublin, and posted placards all over the city inviting every one who owned a pet bird of any sort, size, or pattern to come to a tea party in this hall on a certain day, and bring their favorite bird along with them.

A mortal great gathering it surely was that came to the tea party, bringing all sorts, sizes, shapes, and samples of birds known to creation. And when they had got their tea, the Lord High Mayor said he had a little delightful surprise in store for them. He ordered all windows and doors of the hall to be thrown open, and then asked the audience if they would be so kind as to open their cages and let their birds fly off. At this request there arose a wild uproar, everyone protesting against any such mad proceeding. The Lord High Mayor, he laughed right heartily. Then he produced his whistle and explained, "Ladies and gentlemen, I have got a little magic whistle here, whose virtue is that all birds between the earth's ends must come at its call and alight on my head and shoulders and all around me. I want to honor my own city and people of Dublin by giving them the first exhibition."

When the people heard this, the uproar quashed and they thanked the Lord High Mayor for the honor he was doing them, and they were tumbling over one another in haste to let their birds go.

When the birds were all gone, the Lord High Mayor said, "To give you a real good test of the whistle, we'll wait till the last tail waggles from sight."

Not long they had to wait for that. The goldfinches, blackbirds, canaries, pigeons, and the rest of the clanjaffrey went like a streak o' lightning over chimneys, roofs, and high church-spires.

When the last had disappeared, the Lord High Mayor still took his time before he blew. When he did blow, he said, "Now, lads, look out to see the sight."

They rolled over one another in their hurry to the windows to see the flight of birds returning. And the Lord High Mayor yelled at them to stand back from windows and doors, and give the poor birds a chance to get in again.

"Faith," said they, "there's no sign of them yet."

"There should be," said the Lord High Mayor, "But then, of course, there's a strong high wind blowing today. It may be another quarter-minute before they appear."

A quarter-minute and five quarters went by, and still there wasn't a feather showing. The bird owners began to get a bit uneasy.

Said the Lord High Mayor, "It is that I didn't blow loud enough!"

"We're afeard you didn't," says they.

He went to the window and blew his best this time.

"And now," said he, "watch for the rush."

Though the people watched with all their eyes, neither rush nor crush was coming. And the Lord High Mayor said, "Boys, my wind is weak. Who's the best blower in the room?"

A big butcher took the whistle and nearly blew it in smithers. The Lord High Mayor said, "That's the music that'll fetch them."

But sorrow a wing showed, though the people put their eyes out of the sockets watching.

"Boys," said the Lord High Mayor, "I'm sorry to state it—but I'm afeard there's a mistake somewhere."

And instantly began a roolye-boolye, beside which Bedlam itself was calm as a cloister. With every rioter wanting revenge for his own bird, if a regiment of troopers hadn't ridden into the Hall on horseback, there wouldn't have been two bits left of the Lord High Mayor's corpus. His robes were in flitterjigs.

It took three months and all the doctors in Dublin to make him a whole man again. But it took a fortune from him to buy fresh birds for all the distressed ones. And the Day of the Whistle, as it came to be called, was to be long remembered in Dublin.

The minute he was fit for it, the Lord High Mayor's first order, however, was for the Court to come along with him till he would arrest the rascal, Jack, and have him shot to pieces in the streets of Dublin.

My brave Jack, getting wind of what was waiting for him, got a bladder filled with bullock's blood, and, putting his old mother in bed, tied the contrivance round her neck and pulled up the bedclothes. He was sitting innocently by the fireside, when the dragoons arrived in front of his door, and the Lord High Mayor himself put in his head.

Said the Lord High Mayor, "You villain, I have you at last and will now make you pay with your life for the rascality you wrought on me. Come along, to be shot in the streets of Dublin as an example to all rascals."

Jack said, "And if you shoot me, who am the support of my poor old mother, what will she do for a living?"

"I don't care a horney-button whether she lives or dies," said the Lord High Mayor. "The mother of such a vagabond would be better dead-born, anyhow."

"Well," said Jack, rising up, "I'm willing to go with you. But before I go, I'll have to put my poor old mother at peace." And ere the Lord High Mayor could jump to save the woman, Jack plunged a big knife into her neck, as it were, sending blood spurting to the rafters. The Lord High Mayor, putting a yell from him, said, "Now, you scoundrel, that you have murdered your mother, you deserve your death ten times over!"

"Oh!" said Jack, "if you want to make bones about the killing of an old woman who was half-ways in the grave anyhow, I'll bring her to life again."

"What do you mean?" said the Lord High Mayor.

"I'll show you," said Jack.

And climbing on a stool, he took a cow's horn from between the rafters—a horn that he used to go out on the hill and blow upon to wake the echoes. Down Jack drew it, and, standing in the middle of the floor, blew three blasts. At the first blast, the Lord High Mayor saw the mother move in the bed; at the second she rolled over; and at the third blast, she sat up in bed and called for a bowl of tea.

Said the Lord High Mayor when his speeches came back, "That's the dumfoundingest implement that was ever seen or heard tell of on this earth! Would you sell it?"

"Well," said Jack, "it's such a handy article whenever I lose my temper and take a notion to kill a man for a spell, that I'm loath to part with it."

Said the Lord High Mayor, "I have at home the provokingest wife and stupidest set of servants that ever drove a man to desperation. They madden me a hundred times a day. There's many a time I'd feel it a mighty relief entirely if I could kill a couple or so of them—only it's against the law even for a Lord High Mayor to murder people. But if I had that horn of yours I could slaughter them by the dozen and leave them slaughtered till I cooled off and cared to call them to life again—I'm willing to give you a hundred pounds for it."

Said Jack, "It's sorry I am to part with such a handy horn, but at the same time it's loath I'd be to deny the Lord High Mayor of Dublin anything he demands. So here it is. I bestow it to you for only a hundred pounds."

And the Lord High Mayor had his treasurer pay down to Jack a hundred pounds. And proud as a peacock to have such a valuable horn, back he marched, at the head of his dragoons to Dublin. There he sent messengers to invite in five men whom he wanted to kill, men who had given him a deal of trouble about valuable birds they had lost the Day o' the Whistle. But, not to be wasting time while waiting for these victims, he sent a servant to the kitchen, where his wife was ballyragging the cook, to tell the good woman to halt her tongue, and shut her mouth, and pretend to be a lady. The servant, however, knowing that it wasn't wholesome to carry such an order to his mistress, stood and stuttered.

"What are you standing and stuttering about, you dirty lout?" said the Lord High Mayor, reaching for a big long knife that he had handy.

"I'm afeard," said the servant, "to bring my mistress any such order."

"You are, are you?" said the Lord High Mayor. "Then, by this and by that, you stuttering idiot, I'll soon put the fear out o' you." And he made a stiffey of the servant. To the stair-head then he went, and called to his wife that if she didn't stop her barging and bellowing, he'd step down and teach her good manners.

At three bounds his wife was up the stairs, and facing him.

"What do you mean, Mr. Impudence?" she shouted, "daring to talk that way to me!"

"Here's what I mean," said the Lord High Mayor, leaping at her with the knife—and leaving her a stiffey by the servant's side.

Running his eye round him then to see who was next, he beheld his terrorized valet disappearing out of the door. "Come back here, you ruffian!" shouted the Lord High Mayor.

And the valet, shaking till the teeth in his head rattled, fell on his knees, saying, "My Lord High Mayor, I have never done anything but what was right."

Said the Lord High Mayor, "Do you remember the Monday morning, five years agone, that you forgot to polish my shoes?"

"Oh!" said the valet, clasping his hands in front of him, "I'll only be three years with your Lordship again' Candlemas. It was the fellow before me who forgot."

"No matter for that," said the Lord High Mayor, "if it had been you, you'd have forgotten it all the same. So here's to learn you a lesson you'll not forget for a long time." And he sprang at the valet with the knife—and laid him stiff beside the other two.

The five men whom he had sent for arrived now, expecting they were going to receive big money for the birds he had lost them. They said, "Well, it's time that you'd pay us—you've kept us a long while waiting."

"Yes, you villains," said the Lord High Mayor, "I've kept you a long time waiting, but I'll pay you now. Take that," says he, as he struck one of them, "And take that! and that! and that! and that!" giving the knife to the rest of them, and stretching all five by the sides of them who'd got the early start.

The servants, learning what was happening, ran out of the house and raised an uproar, crying that the Lord High Mayor had gone mad and was murdering all before him. One policeman after another rushed into the house to seize him, till six had gone in. And it was the finest o' fun to his Lordship to lay each of them out stiff as he approached.

The news of the Lord High Mayor's madness and murdering ran like wild fire round Dublin. From street and strand people rushed and ran, making a mighty gathering in front of the Lord High Mayor's Castle—the Bishop and Judge and Commander of the troops heading them.

And the Lord High Mayor, in high good humor at how well his scheme worked—for so far—went out on to the balcony with his horn, and said, "Ladies and gentlemen, and my Lord Bishop, isn't this a mighty pleasant morning?"

"The pleasure has been all on your side, so far," the crowd shouted back. "But come down here, till we hang you."

"Ha! ha! ha! ha!" laughed the Lord High Mayor, right heartily. "Gentlemen and ladies, this is the greatest joke of my life—and when you see the end of it, you'll admit that it is the greatest joke of all your lives. There's a dozen people, more or less, lying stiff dead inside. In my enjoyment I've forgotten the exact count—but two or three, more or less, isn't here or there."

"Where does the joke come in?" shouted the people.

"Here's where the joke comes in," said the Lord High Mayor. "I hold in my hand a horn, three blows from which will make each and every one o' the dead men jump to his feet and call for a bowl of tea. And they'll then be in better health than ever they were in their lives before. This magic horn I have procured at great expense; but as some of you suffered inconvenience, and all of you more or less disappointment and distress, on the last occasion on which I strove to provide innocent diversion for you, I don't mind the outlay, inasmuch as it enables me to entertain and repay you several times over for your former little frustration. As I want you all, without distinction of class, creed, or color to enjoy the festivities I have in store for you, I'll have my servants carry out the dead and lay them in full view, while I recall them to creation again."

The dead ones were accordingly carried out, while the Lord High Mayor stepped about with his horn under his arm, his hands under his coat tails, and he whistling "The Lasses o' Limerick."

"Now," said he, when all was arranged, "before I begin, wouldn't Your Lordship the Bishop, or Your Honor the Judge, or Your Excellency the Commander of the Troops like to come up here and be killed, and have the fun of coming back to life again with the crowd?"

The Bishop and the Judge and the Commander of the Troops thanked him for his consideration, but asked to be excused for various reasons.

"Well," he said, "isn't there some one down there that covets the experience?"

But no, none of them coveted it desperately enough, at the moment. Every one had his own excuse for not being killed and called to life again that particular morning.

"Very well then," said the Lord High Mayor, "we'll have to be content with resurrecting these we have ready. Stand back," he said to the people, "and let the fresh air to the creatures when they start breathing again."

The people crushed back, and the Lord High Mayor put the horn to his lips and blew three blasts.

But, behold you! contrary to all expectation, not one o' the dead ones rose up and called for a bowl of tea. No one of them even twinkled an eyelid.

A roar rose up from the crowd—and the Lord High Mayor himself was a trifle put out. But he explained, "Naturally, I didn't blow loud enough for them to hear me."

"Naturally you didn't," said the crowd, with their knuckles beginning to itch to be at him.

"Well, they'll hear me this time if they were born stone-deaf," said the Lord High Mayor. And he nearly blew the roof off his head.

But none of the dead ones turned a hair, and the crowd put up a yell that was paralyzing.

"Easy! easy!" said the Lord High Mayor, who was getting pale about the gills. "There's some mistake here."

"Faith! yes," said the crowd, starting to climb up for him, "there was a mighty mistake in allowing you to live as long as you have. But," said they, as they caught him, neck and heels, "that'll quickly be remedied." And they bundled him out to be hanged to the handiest lamp post.

It was only through a wonderful wizard from Connacht, appearing on the scene and raising the dead ones to life again, that the troops were able to rescue out of their hands the Lord High Mayor.

Determined now to have the life of the vagabond Jack for certain, the Lord High Mayor never stopped nor stayed till he was at Jack's mother's house with a regiment of dragoons, and had Jack tied into a leathern sack, and slung over the back of a horse, and headed for Dublin—where he had left a hundred men building a fire in the public square for the villain's burning, and a hundred messengers bidding all Dublin to the spectacle—to compensate them for their two previous disappointments.

The royal party, returning with their prey, entered an inn on the outskirts of the city to get refreshments. And my brave Jack, left outside, peeping through a pin-hole in his sack, beheld coming down the road a lubber of a half-Sir, as rich as he was ignorant, who, as all Ireland knew, had for years been nagging the Lord High Mayor, wanting to marry his daughter—and getting kicked out every time.

When Jack saw him, he began lamenting aloud, "I can't marry her, and I'll not marry her, and all the Lord High Mayors in Dublin won't make me marry her!"

"Who's in the sack, and what is he raising this row about?" said the lubber, coming forward.

"I can't marry her, and I'll not marry her, and all the Lord High Mayors in Dublin won't make me marry her!" Jack chanted louder than ever before.

"Who is it that they're forcing you to marry, poor fellow?" inquired the lout.

"Don't you recognize," said Jack, "the Lord High Mayor's horses standing around?"

"I do, but what about that?" said the fellow.

Said Jack, "The Lord High Mayor of Dublin's daughter has taken sudden notion of marrying someone or other, and her father has picked on me, who have no way to support her. So, with his dragoons, he's bringing me to Dublin in a sack, out of which they'll not free me till after the knot's tied so tight that the Pope, himself, couldn't loosen it. She's taking a pig in a poke, to be sure—but—I can't marry her, and I won't marry her, and all the Lord High Mayors in Dublin won't make me marry her!"

The fellow, all excited, cried, "Poor victim! As I have no objection to marrying her, and am rich enough to keep a dozen wives like her, how much will you take to let me into the sack in your stead?"

"I'll let you in for a hundred pounds," said Jack.

"It's a bargain!" said the fellow. And letting Jack out and paying him down a hundred pounds, he got in the sack joyfully and had Jack tie him up safe and secure.

When the Lord High Mayor, beside the bonfire in Dublin Square, and in the presence of the mightiest gathering ever gathered since Adam left the Garden, cut the sack and saw step out of it, instead of Jack, the ignorant idiot who'd been for so long provoking him to get to be his son-in-law, he got in such a frantic fit that one-half of Dublin had to hold him from tossing the fellow into the flames—while the other half started laughing and couldn't stop for a fortnight.

His weight in gold wouldn't induce the Lord High Mayor to go again after the rascal Jack, who, with his hundreds of pounds, built a great castle, married a beautiful princess, and he and his wife and his poor old mother, lived happy and well ever after.

NIDDEN AND DIDDEN AND
DONAL BEG O'NEARY

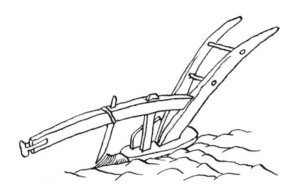

NIDDEN and Didden and Donal Beg O'Neary were three farmers who neighbored one another in the North. Nidden and Didden were great friends, and greedy men both. And ever they envied poor Donal Beg O'Neary anything he possessed. Nidden and Didden had each of them more money than a merchant, while Donal Beg was poor as a partridge in March. However, he owned a cow—just one—which was sleek as a silk hat, and for beauty shamed all the cattle in his neighbors' cowsheds. And what would you have of it but, one night when the devil worked them worse than usual, didn't Nidden and Didden creep into Donal Beg's byre and murder his one cow! When poor Donal Beg in the morning found his cow a corpse, it's the sorry man was he. But to make the best of the worst, he skinned the animal, threw the hide over his shoulder, and off with him to the town to sell it. As he went a magpie lighted on the hide to pick at it, and Donal Beg stretching up his hand, caught the bird and brought it with him to town, expecting to sell it to some child for tuppence.

Donal Beg, entering a tavern at the town's beginning, ordered from the landlady a drink of her best liquor. Says she, as she went to draw the drink, "What are you doing with the magpie?"

"It's a wise companion I have," says Donal, who liked to joke, "who keeps me advised, in its own language, of many things. And," says he, giving the bird a squeeze and making it cry out, "it now tells me that isn't your best liquor that you're drawing from"—for Donal knew of old the woman's deceit.

"That's strange," says the landlady, leaving the keg she was about to draw from and going to another. Donal now squeezed another chatter from the bird and the landlady stopped to ask, "What's it saying now?"

"It's saying," says Donal, "that that's your best liquor at last."

"Well! well! well!" says the landlady, "that bird is the most wonderful wizard that ever was known in this world. Would you sell him?"

"Considering that it knows all things, and advises me of all, I wouldn't part with him easy," says Donal.

"I'll give you a hundred pounds for him," says she.

"By reason that I happen to be in sore need of money at the moment, I'll consent to take it," says Donal.

And she paid down to Donal Beg a hundred golden sovereigns, which he, putting into a bag, carried home—after throwing away the hide.

On that night, Nidden and Didden, to enjoy Donal's grief for the loss of his cow, went after supper to peep in his window. But what, to their dumfounding, did they behold but Donal at table counting a great pile of golden sovereigns! In they went and asked him how on earth he had got hold of such a hoard of money!

Says Donal, "When ye killed my cow on me, ye did me the best turn in all your lives. The King and Queen of France has set the fashion of dressing themselves in cowhides, and all their lords and ladies cannot now get enough cowhides to dress themselves. So, the merchants of the world are going on their knees to anyone who'll fetch and sell them hides for a hundred pounds a piece."

"If that's so," says Nidden and Didden, "it isn't here we should be!" Home with them they dashed, roused up their servants, and spent the night killing and skinning their cows, not leaving one alive to cream their tea in the morning.

At daybreak both were off for the town with cart loads of hides. When they reached the hide merchant's and told him they had a hundred hides for sale, he said he was right glad of that because he'd run out of hides entirely. And he asked them their price.

It seemed to Nidden and Didden that prices should be stiffer today than yesterday, so they answered him that they were asking only two hundred pounds a piece.

When the merchant heard this, he considered he had two crazy men on his hands and sent for the soldiers. Nidden and Didden started arguing with him till a crowd gathered. And when the rabble of the town learnt what they were asking for their hides, they fell on them and tossed them and their cargoes over the bridge into the river, and the hides went out to sea. And Nidden and Didden escaped by swimming for their lives. Then home they hurried to have the life of Donal Beg.

Now Donal, well knowing what would have happened to them and their hides, and well suspecting that the pair of villains would that night be coming for their revenge, he put his old paralyzed mother to sleep in his bed, while he himself slept in his mother's bed.

Sure enough, by midnight Nidden and Didden crept in at the window of Donal's room, murdered the figure in the bed and went home content and happy that they had evened their score with a wicked man.

Very well and good. When Donal got up in the morning and found his old mother murdered and dead he got her in a cart to haul the corpse to the graveyard. Convenient to the graveyard he stopped at a well by the roadside, close to an inn, and lifting his old mother out of the cart, he propped her on two crutches, leaning over the well, and then went to the inn and ordered drinks for two. To the landlord's daughter he says, "I left my old mother getting a drink at the well without. I wish you'd call her in to get a healthier drink here. She's a trifle deaf," he says, "and if she doesn't hear you, give her a shake by the shoulder, and tell your message."

It wasn't long till the landlord's daughter burst into the room again wailing that she had murdered the old woman. "I shook her too hard," she says, "and tumbled her into the well and she drowned! Ochón! Ochón!"

"My sorrow! My sorrow! My poor old mother!" yelled Donal. "Did you drown my poor, dear, old mother? Ochón! Ochón! What'll I do? What'll I do? What'll I ever do, having to live the rest of my days without a mother? It'll be easier for you, little one, because, of course, you'll be hanged for murder and have all your troubles over you!"

"How much will you take," begs the landlord, "and say nothing about it, and save my poor daughter's life from hanging?"

"I'll take three hundred pounds," says Donal Beg, "and cheap at the price, for my poor old mother was all I had in the world." And the landlord was delighted to pay down to him three hundred pounds in gold. They buried the old mother quietly, and Donal Beg went home happy, with the plunder.

After their supper that night, Nidden and Didden went to Donal Beg's, intending now that it was dark and no one would see them, to take out his corpse and bury it. But lo and behold, when they entered, they saw the man they thought they had murdered counting extraordinary heaps of gold at the table!

"What! What! What's the meaning of this?" says they. "Didn't we murder you last night?"

"Oh," says Donal Beg, "last night you thought you did me a bad turn, but instead, you never did better or kinder by me in all your lives before."

"What do you mean?" says they.

"Instead of killing me," Donal says, "you killed, by mistake, my poor old mother—and right sorry I was. But I hoisted her off to the town and sold her for her weight in gold. You maybe didn't hear it—but there's a great war in the East—Hungary fighting China—and both o' them governments are buying up old mothers to make gunpowder, giving their weight in gold for them, and cutting one another's throats to get them at that."

"If that's so," says Nidden and Didden, "it isn't here we should be. We have two old mothers at home who are useless, except for jarring and warring and making life a misery. Why shouldn't we be making our fortune out of them?"

"Ay, why shouldn't you?" says Donal.

Home the two of them dashed without any delay, and murdered their old mothers, and next morning early started off with the corpses for the town. Up and down the streets of the town they searched, with their old mothers over their shoulders, singing out, "Who'll buy old mothers? Who'll buy old mothers for their weight in gold?"

The whole town crowded to the doors and windows for to see the sight and to hear and jeer the two crazy men. The rabble began running after them, chaffing and laughing, and very soon turned to stoning them. So Nidden and Didden had to fire their old mothers over the bridge, take to their heels and run for their lives; and reached home not without plenty of bones broken, and their hearts nigh broken into the bargain.

In the morning they got a sack and started for Donal's house. They said, "To make sure of the conscienceless rascal, this time we'll get him in the sack and drown him in the deepest hole of the river."

Catch Donal they did; tied him up safe in the sack and started for the river. When they reached an inn anigh the river, Nidden and Didden hung the sack on a tree branch outside and went in the inn for refreshments.

Donal Beg, peeping through a pinhole in the sack, saw, coming down the road, a drover with a hundred head of fat cattle, taking them to a fair to sell. And immediately he began to chant—

> "I'm going to Heaven!
> Oh, I'm going to Heaven!
> Isn't it grand to go to Heaven!
> And there's no one going to Heaven but me!"

When the drover heard this he halted and said, "I wish it was me that was going! What will you take to let me go in your place?"

Says Donal, says he, "I wouldn't give up my place for anything less than your drove of cattle and a hundred pounds besides."

"With all the veins o' my heart," says the drover, "I'll give you your asking. Here you are, and let me in!"

"Open the sack then," says Donal. Which the drover did—and letting Donal out, he gave him a hundred pounds and his herd of cattle, got into the sack and begged Donal to tie him tight and safe for the happy journey. Which Donal Beg did, with heart and a half—and then started for home with his hundred pounds and drove of fat cattle.

When Nidden and Didden came out of the inn, they shouldered the sack again, and went on to the river, where they flung their load in the deepest pool and home with them, happy to be rid of the rascal for good-and-all. And right sound they slept that night.

Going forth next morn to partition between them Donal's deserted little place (as they figured), the first sight that nigh blinded their eyes was a hundred head of fat cattle feeding on Donal Beg's hillside, and Donal himself whistling and singing, herding them!

When they came to their cold senses, and to Donal, they said, "How comes it that you're here when we drowned you last night? And how comes all these fine cattle?"

"Oh, my eternal friends," says Donal, "last night you thought you did me a bad turn, but you never did better by me in all your long lives before."

"What do you mean?" they asked.

"Because," Donal answers them, "When you threw me in the river and I sank to the bottom, I found there great meadows and plains stocked with thousands and thousands of the finest and the fattest of cattle the eye of man ever beheld. I had to content me with taking only a hundred of them because I hadn't help to drive more home."

Says they, "Donal, darling, will you come and show us the spot again and help us to get a couple of herds with us?"

"That I will," says Donal, says he, "with right heart and good will."

To the river he started with Nidden and Didden. When they reached it, Donal picked out the very deepest spot and cast in a stone. "Down there," says he, "you'll find the finest and the fattest. In with ye and when you've gathered all ye want, come up and call me."

Nidden and Didden near fought to find which of them would get in first. But Nidden overcame Didden and dived to the deepest part. After a long minute, his head bobbed above the water, and the poor drowning fellow shouted, "Help! Help! Help!" before he went under again.

Says Donal, "He's surely found a treasure of them, when he's asking for help in such a hurry. Stand back and let me down to claim my share."

"No! no! no!" cries Didden. "You've already got your share, bad luck to you! It's my turn now."

"Oh, very well," says Donal. "I never was greedy. In with you, and good luck!"

Didden took a race to the river bank and dived to Nidden's helping.

And my brave Donal came home whistling with light bright heart, took to himself Nidden's wide lands and Didden's bright strands, and ever after lived a wealthy, healthy, happy man — in luxury and ease, no equal for him to be found in all of Ireland's ground.

THE SWORD OF LIGHT

ONCE upon a time, in the long, long ago, a Prince of Tir-Conal died, leaving his castle, his cattle, and all his wealth in gold and silver to his son Fergus, a notorious spendthrift. The father well knew Fergus would quick put scatterment on the fortune, and knowing this, on his deathbed said, "Fergus," said he, "when you have drunk and spent my castle, my cattle, and my wealth, and are down to what is on your back, I want your promise to hang yourself on a certain branch of a certain tree"—naming it—"in the garden."

Fergus promised, and his father died. The father's corpse wasn't cold till Fergus was sowing on the wind all he was worth. A gay time he had of it, while the fortune held—and to the end of everything he came, in good time.

Despair overcame the fellow now, and he saw that his father's advice was a wise one. To the certain branch of the certain tree, Fergus tied a rope, put a noose on it, his neck in the noose, and kicked himself off. But lo and behold! the instant his weight weighed the branch, down it crashed with him, and out from a hole at its butt tumbled piles of gold. It was then glad Fergus blessed his father ten times over for such a wise way of replenishing his fortune.

But though his poor father may have thought otherwise, Fergus's past misfortune was no caution to him. He soon made his new-found wealth vanish—drinking, carousing, and gambling, for a greater gambler again there wasn't to be found between the winds of the world. So, soon came the black day when he hadn't a penny to ring on a tombstone.

Winding home from the gambling house the night he'd lost his last penny, and coming down the hill above his home, swithering what he'd do now at all, at all, he, leaping a ditch, discovered there a big red fellow playing cards, his right hand against his left, and he cursing and arguing fast and furious for this hand or the other—whichsoever he favored.

"Well, well, well!" says Fergus, says he. "That's the drollest thing ever I have seen. What foolishness are you at, anyway?"

"Come, come," says the Big Red Fellow, says he, "sit you down for a game. It's ill off I am for someone to beat, for I haven't got one to play me this seven years, and all that time I've been as ye see me, playing my right hand against my left; and it's no ways fair or fun, for this left hand's so cunning that it's ever and always winning."

"There isn't any use," says Fergus, "in my sitting down, for I haven't a penny between me and poverty."

"Good reason that is, why it's the grandest of all use," says the Red Fellow. "For you may, maybe, win a fortune."

"And what can I stake?" says Fergus.

Says the other, "You'll not be at a loss for that. You can stake your services to me for a year and a day against my granting you —for I have that power from my friend, the Devil—any wish your heart craves for."

Says Fergus, "That's both fair and fortunate—and here's at you!"—planking himself down as he said it.

To the game, then, the pair o' them fell, and it wasn't long till that one was decided, with my brave Fergus winning.

"All right, what's your pleasure?" says the Red Fellow.

"It is," says Fergus, "that my father's castle and court should be mended and repaired from the deplorable state it has fallen into; that there should be servants again in the hall, coaches in the yard, steeds in their stalls, and my father's hills stocked with the hundreds of animals, cattle, and sheep that I've drunk and spent and gambled away."

"Go home," says the Red Fellow. "You have your wish."

And true enough, when my brave Fergus reaches home, there, to his great rejoicement, he finds his father's castle, grander than ever it had been in man's memory. There were liveried servants in the hall, grand coaches in the yard, the stables crammed with steeds, the fairest that ever were driven. And when he gazed from his window in the morn, the sight of cattle and sheep grazing the hills warmed the cockles of his heart.

Reflecting and revelling in his luck, Fergus, the very next midnight, couldn't resist going to the hill, in hopes he might encounter the Red Fellow again. And sure enough, there he was, in the same spot, and at the same racket, his right hand pitted against his left, and he cheating and scolding and blaspheming like a trooper for the one hand or the other, for all he was worth.

"You're hearty welcome," says the Red Fellow. "Sit ye down for a hand at the cards."

'Twas small coaxing Fergus needed. Down he sat, staking the same stake again. And as good luck would have it, he won.

"What's your wish?" says the Red Fellow.

"It is," says Fergus, "that I may have for my wife the beautifullest woman in the world, above ground or below it."

This wish didn't half-please the Red Fellow. He groaned sore, and, says he, "As you won, you'll have your wish, though—sweet bad luck to ye!—that woman I intended for myself."

And when Fergus got home, the beautifullest woman in the world—for surely she was dazzlingly beautiful—was there before him, for wife.

And surely now, he would be happy for life.

Next night his beautiful wife said to him, "I know well you're bent this night on meeting the Red Fellow, but take one word of advice from me. If you win, as I believe you will, let your wish be this, and only this: to have the pick of all horses in his stables; and no matter how many or how grand the horses he'll show you, you are to choose none but the worst-looking, wee, shaggy, brown nag—which he'll do his endeavor not to let with you— that, and the worst-looking saddle and bridle upon it. And then, having got your prize—and I assure you it will be a real prize— never meet the fellow more."

Fergus promised her request, and when he met the Red Fellow that night and they played and he won, and the Red Fellow asked him what was his wish, Fergus said, "My wish is the pick of all horses in your stables."

The Red Fellow, he looked glum for a minute, but then he says, "You'll have your wish."

He put a whistle to his mouth and blew it, and that instant Fergus found himself standing with the Red Fellow in a great stable that had a hundred stalls with a beautiful, shining-black horse in every stall.

"There's the best horses I own," says the Red Fellow. "Which of them will you have?"

"I don't see what I want here," says Fergus. "I'll have none of them."

The Red Fellow looked glum again. He blew on his whistle, and they were now in a stable of a hundred stalls with a beautiful chestnut horse standing in every stall—the loveliest animals that Fergus had ever laid eyes on.

"There's my second best stable," says the Red Fellow. "Which of them animals will you have?"

"There's none of them to my pleasing, I thank you," says Fergus. "Show me some more."

The Fellow was mad now, and says he, "I have no other stable—only one of wee old nags that I wouldn't for shame let anyone see."

"No matter," says Fergus. "Let me see them anyway."

The Fellow was in a red rage, but he blew his whistle, and

they were standing in a stable of a hundred shameful nags. Fergus walked down the row of nags till he came to the very last and worst and shamefullest little nag of them all.

"This one," says Fergus, says he, "is the one for me. And that," says he, pointing to the worst and tornest, dirtiest saddle and bridle on the walls—"that," says he, "is the accoutrement I'll have on it."

The Red Fellow was black in the face with wrath; and says he, "I'll not let from my stables such a shameful animal, nor such disgraceful fittings; I'll never let the like of them be seen by mortal man again."

Says Fergus, "This is my turn to choose, not yours; be they bad or be they good, it's my wish to have them, and since I won the game, my wish is my command."

So, raging mad though he was, the Fellow had to let Fergus saddle and bridle the wee old nag, mount him and away. And, to Fergus's astounding, three leaps of the nag landed him in his own castle yard!

His delightful wife was rejoiced to see him back—"And now," she says, "my brave Fergus, that you have got all in the world your heart can wish for, don't, on the peril of your life, and as I love you, ever more go to meet the Red Fellow or you'll surely rue it. I solemnly warn you."

Fergus promised he wouldn't go near the Fellow again or have anything more to do with him. And he meant it.

But still 'twasn't long till the old craving got the better of him and, unbeknownst to his wife, one midnight he was on the hill again. And the Red Fellow was there, playing his right hand against his left with more riotous commotion than ever.

"You're heartily welcome, Fergus," says he, "Sit you down to a game?"

"It's what I've come for," says Fergus. Down he sat for a game, upon the old terms—and lost! The Red Fellow laughed long and loud.

"For a year and a day now, my lad, you're in my service," says he. "And good service I have for you—which, if you don't perform, will cost ye your head."

"Let me hear," says poor Fergus, "what the service is."

"Hear it you will," says the Red Fellow, "though perform it I'm afeared you never will. It is," says he, "two-pronged: first, to find for me who killed the Knight of Glendore; and to bring to me the Sword of Light, owned by the King of the Eastern World—within a year and a day, or forfeit your honor and your life."

Fergus asked where was the Sword of Light to be found.

"I'll tell you," said the Red Fellow. "The Sword of Light belongs to the King of the Eastern World, who lives ten thousand miles from here. His Castle is surrounded by three walls: the outside wall is a hundred feet high; the next wall, three hundred feet; and the inside wall, nine hundred feet high; and every gate in every wall defies the power of mortal man to get through. The Castle has twelve rooms, one within another, every door of every room guarded by a guard of armed men. The King sleeps in the innermost room, the Sword in its scabbard, riveted to the wall above his head—and if a hand touches it while the King sleeps, it gives three bounds that shake the Castle, and lets three roars that are heard around half the world. But that Sword I must have to fulfill my ambition. There's half a chance in a hundred million that any hero in the wide world can get that Sword, and on that half chance your life is now staked. The Devil's blessing I give you—take it and go!"

With heart weighed down Fergus struggled home, where his lovely wife soon worried him for the secret of his sadness—and he had to tell her.

Then she, heart-stricken, revealed to him that her father was King of the Indies, which lay next to the dominions of the King of the Eastern World, who owned the Sword of Light, the All-conquering Sword of the World. She said the Red Fellow, Gillie Rua of the Hills, the world's worst wizard, had stolen her as a little girl, to raise for his wife, and had stolen from her father, at the same time, the Steed of Swiftness, which for safety he had changed into the appearance of a worthless nag.

With sore heart, she mounted Fergus upon the nag, and before parting, gave him from her finger a ring. She told him to ride to her father's castle in the Indies, and when he showed that ring her father would aid him, all in his power, if any aid was possible —which she sorely doubted. Fergus kissed her and set off.

At every bound the Steed of Swiftness cleared seven hills, seven rills, and seven glens; he could overtake the wind before, and the wind behind couldn't catch him. The steed's toes as he went touched the tips of the highest hills, and the skies parted to let him onward. After a long, long journey, over lands and seas, Fergus at last reached the Castle of the King of the Indies.

The King welcomed Fergus and spread a feast in his honor. When Fergus at the feast filled for the Queen a glass of wine, he dropped in it his wife's ring. And drinking a toast to him, the Queen found the ring, knew it instantly, called on the King to behold it, and demanded how Fergus had come by this token of their long-lost daughter.

Fergus told his story, to their amazing and rejoicing, for when Gillie Rua had carried off their daughter they thought she was lost to them forever.

Nothing now was too good for Fergus. It was like he was Prince of the World. But when the feting and feasting were ended, and the King of the Indies came to consider Fergus's fearful errand, he grieved most sorely. He told Fergus that the wicked Gillie Rua, longtime bent on ruling or ruining the world, now needed for his dread purpose only the Sword of Light.

"You have come," he said, "on a perilous quest. The Gillie Rua commandeered three thousand heroes on that enterprise before you, and no one of them ever came back alive. Still, I'll hope and pray it will be better with you." He said, "I'll give you the best advice I can, anyhow, and do all that's in my power to help you get the information and the Sword. The King of the Eastern World," he says, "who possesses both, lives from here a long day's journey on your nag. What you'll do for a first step," says he, "is start off tomorrow and ride to his Castle. When you get there, leap the outside wall, which is only a hundred feet high, and a pleasure for your Steed. Rattle loud on the second gate and cry a bold demand for the secret, who killed the Knight of Glendore, and for the Sword of Light. Lose no moment then," says he. "Wheel your horse and head for home ahead of the wind! I'll have all our gates open for your entering. If you lose half an instant anywhere, you're a dead man! If you get here alive, we'll then consider the next step."

Fergus promised he would do all this and next morning started out upon his nag. It took seven rills, seven hills, and seven glens at every leap; it caught the wind before, and the wind behind could not catch it. By evening late he reached the astounding Castle of the King of the Eastern World, and putting his nag at the outside wall, a hundred feet high, cleared it. He rattled on the second gate and shouted loud, "I command the King of the Eastern World to tell me the secret, who killed the Knight of Glendore, and to deliver me the Sword of Light."

That instant the gates of the walls and twelve doors of the Castle flew open, and the King of the Eastern World was standing on the Castle's doorstep with a look of thunder on his face.

Fergus, he didn't pause, but putting the nag at the wall again, cleared it and rode home with him ahead of the wind. But the King of the Eastern World was on his heels, flashing the Sword of Light, which dazzled half the world when it was unsheathed. And as Fergus shot through the home-gate a third of his nag's tail was cut off ere the gate clanged behind him. The King and the Queen and all the Court applauded and congratulated Fergus and said that he had surely done well.

"On the morrow," says the King, "you will have to repeat the same performance—only," says he, "you will now find the outside wall fallen, and if you are as successful again, the second wall will come down also."

Well, on the morrow Fergus set out on the nag, did the self-same performance, had the self-same terrific chase after him, and as he and his nag swept through the home-gate another third was shred off the nag's tail! But he was saved. And the second wall was down. And on the third day he went through the same performance once more, and he escaped with the loss of the last third of the nag's tail. But the last wall was down.

The King of the Indies congratulated Fergus. He said, "You're more than fortunate.—When you have done so well so far," says he, "you have a tenth of a tenth of a chance to win through. I'll give you further directions on the morrow, which will be the final and great trial."

Next day, the King gave Fergus the magic Harp of Harps, which he owned, and which Fergus slung over one shoulder. And he gave him a bag of withered beech-leaves, which he slung over the other shoulder, and with them full instructions before setting off upon his nag.

When Fergus reached the Castle of the King of the Eastern World, he began playing upon his harp; whereupon all who heard—the servants, the guards, the soldiers, all—left every post and thronged out and around, listening in wonder and enchantment. When all were collected and their senses enspelled, Fergus scattered before them his bag of beech leaves, which now to their eyes looked like glistening gold pieces. They fell to scrambling and fighting for the riches—leaving Fergus to walk into the Castle and through door after door of twelve open doors, playing as he went—till he reached the innermost room—where the King, enchanted by the music, had fallen into a deep, deep sleep. Fergus entered and quick reached over the King's head for the Sword, giving a powerful pull. But the Sword, resisting, gave three bounds within its scabbard that shook the Castle to its foundation and let out three roars that were heard round half the world. In his sleep the King gave a great start—but didn't awake. Fergus set his teeth, grasped again the hilt, and pulled with all his might. The Sword then leapt and roared—the King bounded in bed, but fell back asleep. The teeth shook and rattled in Fergus' head—but gathering all his nerve and all his strength he gave a third mighty pull. The Castle rocked, the world was deafened, the King sprang awake from his bed! But Fergus had the Sword from its sheath—waved it around his head and demanded to know who killed the Knight of Glendore.

The cowed and trembling King told him what had never been told to mortal man before—the secret that he, himself, it was who

But Fergus had the Sword from its sheath—waved it around his head and demanded to know who killed the Knight of Glendore.

was guilty of the Knight's slaying—and begged for mercy, which Fergus was now only too delighted to yield. And away with himself and the Sword—away before the wind again.

Mighty was the rejoicing when Fergus, with the Sword, got to his father-in-law's! Only, alas! the King of the Indies said, "If now the Gillie Rua gets the Sword of Light, the world and all in it will be given to carnage."

For a sad while the King was silent. Then he said to Fergus, "You are under *geasa* [an obligation that cannot be refused without loss of honor] to fetch him the Sword and the secret—and that you must do. But I'll tell you—bring them to him. When he has got the Sword of Light in his hands, he will flourish it and shout that he's now possessed of the power of the world and the most perfect sword in it. You'll say in reply that it would be the most perfect sword but for one little fault. When he asks what is the fault, you'll reach for the Sword to show him, and when you have it in your hand again, wave it around your head, saying, 'When one waves it like this, it's liable to do damage!'—letting it descend and whip the head off him."

Fergus was rejoiced. He set out upon his nag, for it was now the last day of his service. The nag took seven rills, seven hills, and seven glens at every leap; he overtook the wind before and the wind behind couldn't overtake him—till he came in the presence of the Gillie Rua—who welcomed him.

"It's ten thousand times welcome you are, Fergus," says the Gillie Rua. "For I see you've got the Sword. But have you got the secret?"

"Both of them I have," says Fergus.

"There's the Sword," says he, handing it to him. "And the secret is that it was the King of the Eastern World who killed the Knight of Glendore."

"Hurrah!" says the Gillie Rua of the Hill," taking hold of the Sword and waving it in the air. "I'll soon revenge it—on him and on the world—because I have now all the power of the world and the most perfect sword in it."

"The most perfect 'twould be," says Fergus, "but for one little fault."

"What's that?" says the Gillie Rua.

"I'll show you that and prove it," says Fergus, reaching for the Sword.

"Take note," says he, when he got it—"Take note when you wind the precious object around your head like this, of the damage it's in danger of doing." And with one sweep of the Sword he swept the head from the Fellow's shoulders.

Little time he lost, then, riding home to his wife, who was the rejoiced and delighted woman to see him, and the happiest on earth.

Fergus was now possessed of the beautifullest woman in the world and the most powerful Sword, the Sword of Light, as well as the world's most wonderful Steed, the Steed of Swiftness. His wife's father, the King of the Indies, bestowed on him half his kingdom as his wife's fortune. He was crowned King and she was crowned Queen, and there was feasting for a year and a day. And all the days after, of Fergus and his Queen, were days of joy and gladness.

THE WILL

OF THE WISE MAN

THE time that the Wise Man lived was far longer ago than I could tell you, and twice longer ago than you could tell me. 'Twas a time when wise men were as common as wattle sticks in Ireland, and a fellow couldn't wind his arm without knocking one down. When wise men were so plentiful, he must have been an extraordinary one entirely who'd be called The Wise—as was an old chief by the name of Phelim, who had for his possessions the Wooded Lands of Ardloe, and whose name and fame were notable indeed, and reached the ends of the then-known world. He was named The Wise during his lifetime, and has been known as such ever since—barring for one twelve months during which people called him Phelim the Fool—the reason for which makes this story.

Prince Phelim had four sons, Conal and Donal and Manis and Phelimy Og (or young Phelim). The three eldest, Conal and Donal and Manis, were harum-scarum lads—gamesters and wastrels who never knew God's grace, and were of no account to

King or country. They hunted, sported, and spent, and the world gave in it was their misdoings that brought their poor old father's gray hairs in shame to the grave.

The fourth and youngest son, Phelimy Og, was, on the other hand, the model of what a brave boy and good son should be, and possessed—what was better—a good heart and God's grace. And he was the one stay and comfort of the old man.

That's what made the Wise Man's will, when he died, so strange and such a puzzle to the people—who concluded that, after all, the old saying was a true one, "Call no man a wise man till the worms have done with him."

Many's the man minded this old saw and wagged his head over it when, Phelim being dead and slipped under the sod, his will was opened and read.

For this was the extraordinary way the Wise Man's will went:

"To my eldest son, Conal, I bequeath and bestow all that's green and all that isn't green on the Wooded Lands of Ardloe. To my second son, Donal, I bequeath and bestow all that's crooked and all that's straight on the Wooded Lands of Ardloe. To my third son, Manis, I bequeath and bestow all that moves and all that stands still on the Wooded Lands of Ardloe. And to my youngest son, Phelimy Og, I bequeath and bestow the remainder."

The world, when it heard the will read, was dumfounded, and said that the dead man must surely have taken leave of his senses before he wrote anything so silly. It was bad enough, and dumfounding enough for him, people thought, to leave all of his property to each one of the three sons at the same time; but, after willing away all he owned three times over, to say he bequeathed to Phelimy Og what remained was a sorry joke, and a cruel one to crack at the expense of the poor boy who was his only credit, and who loved and cared for him, and so bravely stuck to him through thick and thin. It passed all comprehending, they said. And they got so mad with the man who was dead that to make up for the favor they had shown him in life, when they miscalled him Phelim the Wise, they then and there christened him Phelim the Fool.

Now the Wooded Lands of Ardloe were the finest game preserve in Ireland, and, on that account, always drew the sports and gamesters of the country. And it was why the dead man, Phelim, had come to call these woods a curse to him instead of a blessin', since the gamesters and sports that they attracted, and the game that they offered, were the very means of spoiling and making good-for-nothin' his three eldest boys. And it was often he prayed God that a hare or a deer might never shake a foot, nor a woodcock call, within their bounds again—prayers that were, to be sure, sadly in vain; for so long as the birds and the animals got here the widest range and closest cover to be found in Ireland, they thronged them and bred like beetles.

'Twas only a few months ere his dying that Phelim the Wise discovered the lands of Ardloe were becoming of rare value, gold being discovered in them, and the engineers pronouncing that it wanted only the clearing away of the woods, which crowded every foot of them, for miners to get to work and make them the richest resource that Ireland ever knew.

But well and good. Phelim the Fool, as we may now call him, wasn't cold in the clay when the wastrels that he left behind him, Conal and Donal and Manis, were at one another's throats fighting like devils for a property whose every foot was now a fortune— the Wooded Lands of Ardloe which each of them claimed had been willed to him, and him alone.

Phelimy Og, poor fellow, as he conceived he had no claim whatsomever in the matter, left the three good-for-nothings to settle the dispute among themselves and went to the King, who had been a good friend of his father's, to apply for a job by which he could feed and clothe himself and live in modest decency. And the King, taking pity on him, gave him the post of undergroom in his stables, to which Phelimy went, grateful and thankful, not worrying the world with any complaint he had against it, but prepared to spend, from that day forward, a hardworking, industrious life.

Conal and Donal and Manis, when they had long enough disputed with small signs of agreeing, came at last into the City of Armagh, where the King had his Court, put their case before him, and asked him to decide what was just between them. But when he read the will, he was a nonplussed man. He shook his head and told them to go farther, for that the document flabbergasted him out and out, though he was a king.

"And what are we to do?" they asked.

"If you don't divide into three equal parts, and share and share alike," says the King, says he, "the Wooded Lands of Ardloe, I don't know what else you can do."

"I'll not share and share alike with anyone in a property that, as you see set down in black and white, has been willed to me entirely," says Conal.

"I'll not share and share alike with man or mortal in a property that has been entirely willed to me, as a blind man may see for himself," says Donal.

"And I'm very sure," says Manis, says he, "that I'm not such a fool as to share and share alike with soul or sinner in the Wooded Lands of Ardloe that have by that written parchment been put into my whole, sole, and complete possession. It's in a lunatic asylum and not at large I ought to be," says he, "if I turned such a trick."

"Well! Well!" says the King, says he. "There's nothing for it but to take your case afore the judges. As they're wiser than all other men in these matters, and accustomed to clearing up contrairy wills, if there's any reding of the riddle, they'll rede it."

The King, he sent out messengers to the first and greatest judges in his dominions, calling them to come into Armagh immediately and sit upon an extraordinary case which had come up for decision. And in short time judges were crowding into the city, walking, running, and riding. And the King himself went down to the Courts when they sat, and all the people of the City of Armagh that could find standing room crowded the Courts also; for all of them had learned of the comical will of Phelim the Fool, and came in wonderment to hear what the judges would make out of it. And Conal and Donal and Manis were there, every one of them, to state his case—with dozens of witnesses, and counselors by the score, ready to prove that black was white, and white was grogram gray, or anything else needful. And on the case, the great and noble judges of the Kingdom of Armagh, with the great, wise High Chief Judge himself over them all, sat for seven days and seven nights, hearing, deliberating, argufying, sleeping in relays where they sat, and taking their meals from their fists without quitting the Bench. And the excitement in the Court and the City of Armagh, and over all the country around, was tremendous, and grew greater and greater as the case proceeded, till at last the people threatened to mutiny and rebel, and rise out and slaughter all before them if the Judges of the High Court didn't soon come to a decision, and a proper one, and one that would satisfy everybody. And the very King himself got mortal afraid.

But lo and behold ye! At the end of seven days and seven nights, when everything that could be said in the case, and that couldn't be said in it, everything that bore on it, and everything that didn't bear on it was heard and proven, the distracted judges asked for an hour's peace, to consider their final decision—which was granted them. And the people waited without drawing their breaths to hear what would come of it. But, behold, before half of the hour was up, the officer at the door of the room where the judges had retired had to send for the soldiers, to rid the judges out of one another! And no two of them could be allowed to lodge in the same street that night.

The people got in a terrible way entirely. And it took all that the King and his Counselors could do to soothe them and keep them from breaking out and slaying all coming their way. Many of them didn't go to bed at all, and couldn't sleep if they did go to bed. But they paraded the streets, cursing the law and the lawyers, and singing rebellious songs, and kicking up the frightfullest hullabaloo that had been heard in the city of Armagh since the day it was christened.

Toward break o' day they gathered in the center square and, to mark their aggravation at the judges, agreed that the first man to enter the city gates in the morning, though he be a lunatic, or a traveling tinker, should be made High Chief Judge over the City and the Kingdom of Armagh for a year and a day. And they'd put him in the High Judge's robes, and set him in the High

Judge's place, and bring all their troublesome cases to him.

The King, who by now sorely spited the judges himself, right heartily gave his consent, which mollified them one and all, and restored order, and gave the soldiers control of the city again afore the day dawned .

At break o' day they were one and all assembled at the city gate, watching for the first wayfarer who'd be lucky enough to come along. And the sun had hardly begun pushing its shoulder over the hill when, in the far distance, along the white road, they saw a speck coming, getting larger and larger, till at length they made a man out of it. The excitement grew great as he came nearer, they waiting and watching and trying for to know his appearance and features, and to guess what he was at all. And when he at length had come so close that they could make out a little dark countryman, dressed in homespuns, and with his belongings in a red handkerchief stuck on a stick overshoulder, they put up such a cheer as reached, far off, the little man, bringing him to a standstill in wonder.

This man was no other than one named in his own far-off neighborhood, Dark Patrick—a plain, little, low-set, stout-built man, with an eye like an eagle's, black hair, and a black, bushy beard—which was why he was called Dark Patrick. He lived all alone by himself in a little hut of a house in a Donegal mountain glen—and he was noted, not only among his neighbors, but far and wide, for twenty miles every way, for his country wisdom, the benefits of which he gave free to all his neighbors and to all who came to consult him. And 'twas many's the client he had, for in every case of difficulty and doubt that anyone got into within twenty miles of the little man's hut, it's spit on his stick he'd do of a morning—and off to see Dark Patrick on the matter, laying the needs and difficulties of the case afore him, and getting his directions and guidance. And 'twasn't once in a dozen times that these poor people found they were misguided; for the extraordinary counsel that would be given by that plain little man—who was as poor as themselves and carried himself humbler than most of them—was never proved by time and circumstance to be other than correct. And the people of the mountains loved him and gave him as much respect as if he'd been a King instead of a poor struggling creature, delving and digging from June to June, trying to wring a living from a niggard patch.

When Dark Patrick reached the gates, they questioned him who he was, and what; and where he was traveling to. And he answered them that he was a poor man from Donegal, his name Patrick; and he was pushing to Armagh, he said, to see the King regarding a bit of bog that he had always depended upon for his winter's firing, but which a rich man, to whom the whole bog was of small account, now wanted to deprive him of.

"Well," says they, "though you've come for a bit of bog, the King's been waitin' to put you in the place of his High Chief Judge, dress you in satin robes, and let you sit for a year and a day in his High Court, administering justice between man and man."

Dark Patrick replied to them that he was worn after his long tramp from Donegal and in small spirit for joking; and that, moreover, the citizens of the King's own City were surely too honorable and hospitable to make fun of a poor stranger come into their midst. "Let me get on," says he, "to see the King, and start home again, for I'm a simple mountainy man, not used to city ways. It's seldom I ever lose sight of my own chimney, and when I do I'm ill at ease till it's with me again."

They laughed hearty at this, and said he was the man of all men they were lookin' for. And a couple of big fellows of them hoisted Dark Patrick on their shoulders and started off, followed by a tremendous crowd, roaring and cheering, and a man in the forefront, carrying a banner on which they'd written in large letters: "WELCOME, WELCOME TO OUR NEW HIGH CHIEF JUDGE!"

The King, grateful for anything that put his people in good humor again, ordered Patrick to be lodged in the Head Inn of the town, treated to the best, and restored after his long journey, and afterward put upon the Bench to fill the space that all the judges, now in disgrace, showed themselves unfit to fill. "This poor man from the mountains," says he, "mayn't be much of a lawyer, nor have half a head, nor average wisdom about him, but I'll guarantee he's no worse than the dunces that have been disgracing my Bench." And these judges were one and all that hour dismissed from the King's service.

Patrick was whisked off, and shoved into the Head Inn, and the King's orders given to the landlord that he was to treat him same as if he was a gentleman. And on the very next morning the crowd—who'd now got into good humor again—came early to carry the countryman back to the Courts and have their fun with him. There wasn't a bit of use in Patrick's protesting. They hoisted him on their shoulders, and away, with a mighty multitude cheering behind.

The King had come down to the Court himself to enjoy the fun, also. He had a front seat in the gallery, and when Patrick was put on the Bench, and the Court was jammed, crammed, and rammed with every soul it could hold without bursting, the Court Crier called out and asked if there was anyone had any case to bring forward and put before their new High Chief Judge. And it struck the King that it would be a grand joke, entirely, for to put before the poor mountain man the will of Phelim the Fool, and ask him to decide it.

So he spoke out, and asked why shouldn't the Will Case that the disgraced judges had failed to settle be put before their new High Chief Judge, to find what would be his verdict? The crowd roared with delight at the grand idea, and shouted, "The Will Case! The Will Case! Bring Phelim the Fool's Will Case before him!"

Now, the little dark man upon the Bench had been fidgeting and feeling mighty embarrassed at having to supply amusement to the great City of Armagh. But when Phelim the Fool's will was produced, and the chief lawyer in the Court began reading it to him, it was noticed that all of a sudden he got interested—and was soon leaning forward, very attentive, entirely. And as the lawyer went on with the reading, Patrick shoved off him the ridiculous robes they put him into, and sat so sedately, and listened with such intelligence that the crowd in the Court, and even the King himself, stopped their laughing and joking, and began to get interested themselves watching the face of the man who sat on the Bench in homespuns.

When the will was done reading there was silence in the Court, everyone holding his breath to hear what Dark Patrick would say. And he asked, "Are the contestants of this will here?"

"They are," says the people, and they pushed forward Conal and Donal and Manis. Each one of the boys stated his case, solemn and brave, and particularly pointed out how ten times more valuable the property had become by reason of the gold discovered under; and proved, each to his own satisfaction, that the Wooded Lands of Ardloe belonged to him and him alone.

The little man upon the Bench was scanning each one of them very sharply as they gave their evidence—never saying one word or asking one question, but letting them ramble on till they were finished. And the people were wondering mightily at Patrick's self-possession—as was also the King.

"My three good boys," says Dark Patrick, says he, when the three brothers had finished their statements, "I should like to ask ye one question."

"Surely," says they, politely. For in spite of themselves, like every other body in the Court, they'd somehow taken on respect for the little dark mountain man sitting on the Bench. "Surely," says they, "a hundred questions if ye like."

"Thank you," says the little man on the Bench, "but one will be sufficient—tell me," says he, "how have you three fine, brave, able-looking boys been supporting yourselves, and helping and comforting your father since you came to the years of sense?"

The three lads, a good deal staggered, hemmed and hawed, and said a good deal without saying anything—till the little man, when he was tired listening to their mumbling, spoke out, and asked if any dependable person in the Court would come forward and answer for him the question that these lads seemed so tedious about replying to. The King himself, no less, got on his legs, and told Patrick the truth of the matter, and the sort of gamesters an' hunters an' spendthrifts these lads had ever been, and that it was the world's wonder why their poor father, whose heart they had broken, ever willed them anything. But since he did will it so, law was law, and not people's liking. So the silly will must be administered.

"Humph!" says Patrick, says he, "I thank Your Majesty— And will Your Majesty please tell me," says he, "where's the fourth party named in this will—Phelimy Og, if I don't mistake the name—and what's his character?"

"Oh," says the King, says he, "he is earning his day's wage as undergroom in my stables. Don't bother about him, since his father bequeathed him nothing. Decide the case," says he, "if you can, as between the three men that have claims on it, for it's too much time and temper has been wasted over it already."

Says Dark Patrick, says he, "I'm a peculiar kind of a man, and when I take a notion I like to be humored in it. I'm anxious to hear the character of this Phelimy Og—what sort of a son he was, and how he spent his time."

"Oh!" says the King, says he, "so far as that goes, the poor fellow was all right." And he went on to tell about the good son Phelimy was, and to lament that his unnatural father left to him nothing but a joke.

"Will Your Majesty please send for Phelimy Og, then, till he too hears my verdict?" says Dark Patrick, says he. The King was getting impatient, but someone advised him it was better to humor the little man on the Bench anyway.

So Phelimy Og was sent for and came into Court breathless, getting his arms into his coat as he came, and running his fingers through his hair to look decent—for Phelimy was working like a black at his new job.

Dark Patrick ordered him to stand up at the bar, in line with his three brothers. And Phelimy, not knowing what was to happen, did as he was bid. And the three brothers, dressed up in the smartest and finest, with their hair shining, cast scornful glances down at Phelimy, who, too much ashamed and too bashful to look up at them, cast his eyes to the ground.

There was a terrible silence entirely in the Court now, and every man was listening to his own heart beating. And the most eager and anxious man there was the King's own self, him leaning so far forward out of the seat on which he sat that a couple of people neighboring him put out their hands to keep him from falling over.

Dark Patrick sat back in his seat on the Bench, and looking and speaking, same as if he was sitting among the neighbors by his own fireside in Donegal, began to give his verdict.

He said, "Your Majesty, and good people all, I have read this will made by him that you have nicknamed Phelim the Fool, and that I call Phelim the Very Wise—read this will, and heard this case, which is as plain as the meadows o' Meath; and have come to the decision which no man can dispute."

"What is it?" says the King, terribly eager.

"It's what I'm coming to, Your Majesty," says Dark Patrick, calm and respectful. And the King looked small for a minute. "My decision," says Dark Patrick, "is that the Wooded Lands of Ardloe are, most deservedly, willed into the whole, sole, and complete possession of you, Phelimy Og."

Everyone in the Court started, from the King down to Phelimy Og himself.

"It's a lie!" says a hundred angry voices, all at once. "It's a lie! Throw him down!"

Says Dark Patrick, without moving an eyelid, "Since I've been appointed High Chief Judge by His Majesty, sitting there, I, in my capacity as High Chief Judge, will take insult from no man—crowned or uncrowned," he added. "I order the soldiers here to put under arrest the next man guilty of contempt of Court, and I defy disobedience."

Even the King, he bowed his head to this. Unless he scouted his own laws, he had to acknowledge that the little dark mountain man on the Bench had the upper hand even of himself.

"On your peril, keep quiet," says the King, says he, to all his subjects in the Court.

Dark Patrick, no way affected, took up his speech again. "To you, Phelimy Og," says he, nodding his head to Phelimy, "is willed, as I said, all the lands of Ardloe. Now, Conal, this document here says that to you belongs all that is green and all that isn't green *on* the Wooded Lands of Ardloe. Please take particular heed to that very little, yet very important, word, '*on*.'— Very good. And to you, Donal, this document wills all that is crooked and all that is straight *on* the Wooded Lands of Ardloe

—Very good again. And to you, Manis, I here see willed all that moves and all that stands still *on* the Wooded Lands of Ardloe. That is to say, every blade of grass, every stick of timber, every fin of fish, every feather of bird, and every foot of animal on the Wooded Lands of Ardloe is the property of you, Conal, Donal, and Manis—and for them, every one of you is by law individually responsible. Since your poor father died, the three of you have been trespassers and lawbreakers, in leaving your grass and trees growing, your fish swimming, your birds flying, and animals running on the Wooded Lands of Ardloe, the property of your youngest brother, Phelimy Og, to whom is here willed all your father's possessions, barring the living and growing things thereon."

There was a great silence entirely in the Court.

Says Dark Patrick, "As the Woods of Ardloe, with all the sporting they supplied, have been so long the ruination of the three of you elder boys, your more-than-wise father very wisely decided that they should be your ruination no longer. But he wisely willed that you should profit by being, yourselves, the instruments for their destruction. Every hour, henceforth, that you allow one of your sticks to stand, or one of your hares to run, upon Ardloe, you are liable to, and must receive, imprisonment, for being deliberate and malicious trespassers. He has wisely willed that you shall have wholesale work to do clearing these lands, and opportunity to reflect upon your useless lives, and that you'll serve the good brother and faithful son whom you drove out—clearing the way for his prospectors and miners to get to work and unearth his wealth. "Go," he said, "on your peril lose no single day till you have begun this useful work, that the will and the law now commits you to . . . What's the next case?" says Dark Patrick.

But the furor that instantly got up in that Courthouse, and the deafening cheer after cheer that was raised, forbade anyone thinking of any other case. The King himself got up in his box and led the cheers, himself cheering louder and longer than any man there. And as soon as things calmed down, which wasn't for a long time, and during all of which Dark Patrick sat patiently and quietly and humbly—when things calmed, and he could make himself heard, the King spoke out in the presence of all, and said to Dark Patrick, "I here and now name you as my High Chief Judge, not for a year and a day, but for all the years ever you live, and may they be many. Moreover, I here and now, in the presence of all witnesses, offer you any three requests you choose to name. What are they?"

"Your Majesty," says Dark Patrick, getting to his feet, and speaking very respectful—"Your Majesty," says he, "is very, very kind, indeed, to a poor ignorant man from the hills of Donegal, and I feel accordingly grateful. As you have made me such a handsome offer in asking me to name any three requests I choose, I shall take you at your word. My first request," says he, "is that you here and now relieve me of an office that I'm not fitted for, and that has been put upon me without my consent. My second, that you will instill into your people that it is unmanly and unworthy to make their fun at the expense of the poor and the stranger coming within your gates. And the third is that for which I traveled to see you all the way from Donegal—namely, that you'll confirm me in the possession of a little patch of bog from which I every year cut my winter's fire, and which a rich man now covets and strives to grab from me. If you grant me these, my three dearest requests,—and I know you will, for an honorable king like you never breaks his word—I'll be grateful to you while I live."

Both the King and the crowd were consternated when they heard his requests, and the people called upon the King to break his word. But Dark Patrick only shook his head, no matter what remonstrances were made, and the King, seeing how concerned was Patrick, and determined, had to grant him his three requests. And Dark Patrick, respectfully refusing all offers of money and costly presents that the King and people wanted to shower upon him, said to them that these things, while they were of value to the generous givers, were of no value whatsoever to him, who lived plainly and humbly in a little cabin upon a patch of land where he always got enough to eat and sufficient to clothe him, and was now, too, always assured of plenty of fire to keep him warm between summer and summer.

"And I have there," he said, "peace, content, and love of my neighbors. These, with a hillside of my own, health, and a spade, make me the wealthiest man in the whole world. Good-bye! God's blessing be with you all, always."

And mounting his bundle upon his staff, the little dark countryman in his homespuns, went out of their gates, and headed along the white road that pointed for the mountains of Donegal.

THE MAD MAN,
THE DEAD MAN, AND
THE DEVIL

On the northeast side of the hill of Harney are three lengths of land, running from where the hill hits the sky down to the burn that croons an old Gaelic tune at its bottom—and these three sizable strips form three brave farms that are known for fifty miles on every side by no other name, fame, or title than the Mad Man's Farm, the Dead Man's Farm, and the Devil's—and each succeeding son that heirs the land is known as Johnny the Mad Man, Mickey the Dead Man, Danny the Devil—or whatever their given names may be.

And strange, entirely, it is, how these same farms first came by the nicknames that'll stick to them while grass grows, water flows, and crows put out their tongues.

Maybe 'tis a hundred years ago now—maybe more and maybe less—since there were three brothers, Conal, Donal, and Teague, who owned and worked the farms that their father had split among them—and they were married to three neighbor women, sisters. Wise, able, witty women they were, more betoken, their equal not to be discovered by a man on a race horse throughout June's Long Day.

Upon a memorable day, these three sisters met at the Fair of Farney, foregathering in a public inn to trade the news, to gossip of their husbands, sample a jorum, and eat a bite would bar the lonesomeness from their stomachs till they'd reach home. When they got served, says the waiter who attended them, "Who pays for this?" And answers one of them, winking at the other two, "The Good Lord above'll pay,"—meaning, of course, the Good Man of the Sky.

Off the *gomeral* [fool] of a waiter goes, upstairs with him three steps at a bound, and requested settlement of the three women's score from Lord Kilcar, landlord of all the country-side, who at that minute was surrounding both a dinner and a bottle in the room overhead. And in three flips of a lamb's lug, Lord Kilcar, mad as a drawn badger, was down to the three merry women in the public room.

"What! What!" says he, "What's the meaning of this impudence I'm hearing? Why do you presume my Lordship to be such a fool as to pay for the dinners of three huzzies whom I never saw before and, I hope, will never see again?"

The three of them laughed heartily at the waiter's blunder. Then says the same woman again, winking at the others, "We didn't take you to be any bigger fool than the rest of the men. Ye are all much of a muchness, like Danny Doolin's 'tatties the year they forgot to grow to a size."

"Are ye married women?" asks the Lord.

"Yes, unfortunately!" says she.

"And do ye stop to think how you reflect on the misfortunate men who own ye?" says he.

"All men are fools," says she, "the only difference being that the men who own us are the biggest fools of all!"

"Who are the unlucky men?" asks Lord Kilcar.

"They are your three tenants on Harney Hill," says she, "Conal, Donal, and Teague O'Hara."

"The three wisest men in the barony," says the Lord. "By the powers," says he. "I'll make you prove your words or pay for them! Within a week, if you haven't demonstrated to me and to the world that your three daicent men are fools, I'll dispossess each and all from your farms on Harney Hill and leave you take the world for your pillow."

No way daunted, the first woman says to him, "And if we do prove it, what'll be our reward?"

"I'll give you," says the Lord, "the farms you sit in, free from all rent, cess, cut, or tax forevermore. I might as easy," he added, "promise you all I'm worth in the world, for ye'll never earn it," says he.

"Don't shout till ye're out of the wood," says the witty one, says she, winking again at the other pair, who winked back to her. For there wasn't a jokinger, heartier three women in the parish or the next to it than these same.

Lord Kilcar shook hands with them on the bargain, and in admiration for their bravery, settled their score with the waiter. And the gay ones trudged home, laughing, light-hearted, and happy.

Now Conal, Donal, and Teague O'Hara were three who always ate a hearty dinner and would throw their head on the bed to have a good snooze, after. On the very next day, when Conal was having his forty winks, his wife flour-whited his face, covered him with a white sheet, and set up lighted candles alongside.

For Donal, when he was asleep in his own house at the same time, his wife, with pots of paint, made a black man out of him, made red rings round the eyes, red corners to his mouth, and put horns on his head.

Teague's wife gave her man, for his dinner, 'tatties which she told him were cabbages, a white trout which she said was a pig's cheek, and a jug of buttermilk that she swore to be a jug of punch. Teague at first laughed at a joke, but when he found she stayed solemn as a preacher, he got mad and told her either *she* was gone crazy or else *he* was—and he went off to his sleep in a tantrum.

When Conal awoke and looked 'round him, and saw the candles lit and the bed draped, he let a bellow out of him. "Molly! Molly!" he yelled. "What's the matter here?"

"Whisht! Whisht!" says Molly, says she, very grave, "and lie down with ye—don't ye know that ye're dead?"

"Dead!" says he. "What are ye blatherin' about? Wasn't I livin' when I went to sleep, not an hour ago?"

"Ay, poor fellow, God help ye!" says she. "'Tis many's the poor man had the same story to tell—lay down well and hearty and woke up dead! Och! och! och!" says she, covering her face with her apron, and her body shaking. "Och! och! och! the Lord pity poor me, so sudden left a widda!"

"Molly, Molly!" says Conal, provoked, "what humbug are ye at, anyway?"

"And," went on Molly, her face buried and her body shaking, "'tis the kind man ye were to me, Donal, when ye were in this life, and I implore the Lord to deal kindly with you in the world you're now in."

"Quit yer blatherskite," says the angry man, says he, "or ye'll drive me mad!" He bounded out of bed and to the looking-glass; and when he saw himself white and ghastly, put a screech out of him!

"Molly, dear, dear Molly," he pleaded—with a color of hope in his voice—"you don't railly mean for to say that I'm dead, sure you don't?"

"Yes, poor fellow, God have mercy on your soul!" says she. "Died paicefully and sweetly last night on the stroke of midnight. Mickey, the carpenter, took your measure this morning, and I'm expecting your wooden suit any minute. It would be most unseemly for any daicent corp to be seen wandering, so, I beg of you, poor fellow, to compose yourself on the bed again."

"Och, och, och!" says Conal, says he, "ye can't railly mean it that I'm dead, out and out?"

"When you were in this world, Conal," says Molly, "it was the divil's own job to convince ye of anything you didn't want to be convinced of, and I see that the other world hasn't improved ye. But," says she, "if ye don't believe me, look from the window."

The minute he did, he put from him a screech that near tore away a piece of the roof. And says he, "The Divil! the Divil! the Divil's coming for me!"

"Yes, poor fellow," says Molly, "all I could do with ye when ye were in this life, you would persist in card-playing on Sundays, and here's the Divil now, sure enough coming to claim you."

It was Donal, made the devil by his wife, that was coming, bounding to them.

For when Donal had woke from his sleep, and that his wife, pretending to be in terrible fright, told him he wasn't her man at all, at all, but the Devil; and that he, after ballyragging her for taking leave of her senses, looked in the glass and saw himself the dead spit of the devil, he didn't know what under the heavens had happened—but as he always went to his elder brother Conal for consultation in all difficulties, with a leap and a skip, he was out of the house and at top speed heading for Conal's to get that wise man to tell him truly was he the Devil or wasn't he.

But now Conal, when he saw the Devil coming for him, gave a leap and a screech and out of the house, heading like a hare for Teague's house for protection. When Donal saw Conal run from him, he shouted piteously, "Wait! wait for me, Conal O'Hara, I want ye!"

At this, Conal put from him an unearthly yell, and, "Sure enough," says the poor fellow to himself, "it isn't alone dead I am, but damned, when the Devil's wanting me!" And he doubled his speed to get away from his pursuer.

"Wait for me! Wait for me! Conal O'Hara!" Donal would shout. And Conal, at each call, would roar frightfuller and run faster.

"Sure enough," at last says poor Donal, says he to himself, "I *am* the Devil, when Conal, whom I believed my brother, is frightened by me into fits!"

Teague, poor man, was awakened from his sleep by a crash

"Wait for me! Wait for me! Conal O'Hara!" Donal would shout.
And Conal, at each call, would roar frightfuller and run faster.

like the crack of doom, when his brother Conal burst through the door. He sat up in bed, his eyes the size of small tea cups, staring at the vision.

"What under the sun is the meanin' o' this?" he cried. "Or what in the name of wonder has come over ye, Conal?"

"Save me, Teague! Save me!" cried Conal piteously. "I'm dead —died last night—and the Divil is at me heels, to take me—to take me to Hell!"

In of the house at this instant burst Donal. Conal, with a screech would waken a graveyard, dived under the bed and disappeared.

"Ay, the Lord help me," said Teague, "the poor woman was right, after all—I must be crazy complete, when I think I see a dead man walking and talking, and the Divil after him. And why, oh why, do they let me run loose this way, a danger to the public! 'Tisn't here I should be, but in the madhouse. I'm more sensible in this than them who think themselves sane."

"And I'm sure," says Donal, hearing Teague's complaint—"I'm sure I have sense enough to know that 'tisn't here I should be, but in Hell."

"And," says Conal, shoving his head from under the bed, "I'm very sure that 'tisn't under the bed is the respectable place for a corp—but daicently in my grave. It's scandalous," says he, "to leave me exposed, and the weather so hot."

Then off the three of them started, every one his own way, heading for his own right place.

When Teague came to the madhouse, the keeper, after only two minutes' talk with him, agreed that he surely must be one of the maddest men he had ever encountered.

"But," says he, "I can't let you in here without a Magistrate's order."

As Lord Kilcar was a Magistrate, Teague then headed for him.

Conal, he never stopped till he was at the graveyard, and told the gravedigger he was come to be buried. The gravedigger, alarmed, tried to persuade Conal that it was living he was, and not dead; but Conal got so mad-angry at the fellow's doubting his word that he was in mind to give him the father and mother of a sound thrashing.

"Well," pleaded the trembling gravedigger, "I'm forbidden to bury a body without a certificate of death. You'll have to go to Lord Kilcar who signs such documents."

So off Conal started to get his death certificate from Lord Kilcar.

Donal, when he started for his destination, remembered that he'd forgot where, exactly, it was located; so he tried several houses, one after another, inquiring the way to Hell—causing the people to fly out of doors, windows, and chimneys. And very soon the whole countryside was galloping hurry-scurry over hill and dale, with the black fellow pursuing, begging them, for Heaven's sake, to direct a poor strayed Devil the right way to his own Place. Till at last, one poor fellow, cornered and couldn't escape told him. "None of us here is l'arned enough in joggraphy to direct you. You'll have to go ask Lord Kilcar, who knows everything. If anybody knows how to go to Hell, he does."

So off for Lord Kilcar Donal likewise headed.

Lord Kilcar didn't know whether it was his head or his heels he was on, when three crazy creatures gathered on him, one begging an order of admission to the lunatic asylum, the next asking him to make a decent corp of him by giving him a certificate that would get him the grave he needed, and the third beseeching that he'd give him proper directions on the nearest way to Hell.

"'Tis on-Christianlike," says Donal, "that people let a poor Devil wander here, friendless and forlorn, and won't tell him the way to where he rightfully belongs."

"And," says Conal, "I wouldn't complain so much myself, only the weather is such that it'll not be good for either man or beast if I'm left above ground any longer."

And says Teague, "Myself's seeing such strange things everywhere that if I'm not got quick in the madhouse and into their strongest straightjacket, I'll not be responsible for what I may do."

"Bad luck to you!" says Conal, hitting Teague a *poltog* [a blow with the fist] in the stomach. "You can't be in the madhouse too soon. Haven't ye sense enough to stand off my corns?"

"Ye dirty corpse, ye!" says Teague, letting go a *poltog* at Conal. "'Tis small wonder there's madmen in the world when the likes o' you are allowed out wandering the world!"

"'Tisn't half so bad as the likes of you to be left loose, ye lunatic, ye!" says Conal, reaching one back again for Teague.

"Whisht, whisht! and behave yourselves like Christians, ye two onmannerly bears!" says Donal, stepping in to make peace. "If ye don't hold your whisht, I'll carry the both of ye with me to Hell—after his Lordship tells me where it is."

"Gentlemen! gentlemen! for Heaven's sake," begged poor frightened, distracted Lord Kilcar. "Keep peace and don't make smithereens of my house and all's in it. Conal, Donal and Teague," says he, "there's some sad mistake somewhere. I beg of ye to go home to your wives and children like daicent, respectable men."

The three of them thereupon raised an uproar greater than ever marked the Fair o' Farney.

"Are you going to deny a poor graveless corp his certificate of death?" says Conal.

"Is it you refuse a friendless poor lunatic an order on the madhouse?" says Teague.

"Would you be so on-Christianlike," says Donal, "as not to direct a poor Devil the right way to Hell?"

Lord Kilcar was disordered and dumfounded. They'd neither hold their tongues nor take their leave, and the clang and clamor was every minute more unendurable, each of them striving to raise his shout above the other, demanding his own requirement. Till the poor Lord saw at last that he must send for their wives to get sense into their heads and take them off him.

Then he begged them to be patient and quiet for one hour's time, and he'd have for them everything they wanted.

"If I've got to wait an hour," says Conal, "it would be most onseemly before the world to see a corp sitting in a chair. I must have a coffin to stretch in."

"And," says Teague, "I'm sure it would be every bit as onbecoming if a stranger came in and find me here, loose. I must be locked in a padded room."

"And," says Donal, "do you think I have no shame in me at all? If I've got to wait an hour, I must be let sit on the coals."

The distracted Lord Kilcar, poor man, had to lay out Conal in a large pigs' trough. Teague he locked in a cupboard. And he got a coal stove painted red, where Donal mounted, hunkered, and hugged himself for the downright comfort of it. Says he, "And they tried to tell me I wasn't the Devil! This red-hot stove doesn't take a feather out o' me."

And that's how their wives found the three lads when they arrived, and Lord Kilcar beseeched them for sake of the Lord in Heaven to take away their lunatic husbands, and to take, likewise, the law papers he had quick readied, granting them their lands rent-free while winds blew and cocks crew. "I heartily agree," says he, "that you've proved your husbands to be as three great fools as walk the world—and I'm only afeared that if I don't get ye away from me, quick and fast, you'll prove meself the biggest fool of the four!"

"What'll ye give us, if we do?" says Conal's wife, winking at the others.

Cried the suffering, poor man, trembly, "Nobbut, I'll give ye a hundred pound apiece to stock your free farms, if ye don't—if ye'll only promise to go off instantly, quietly, taking your lunatics with ye, and never to come next or near me again. Here ye are!" And to every woman of them, along with the title deeds, he handed a hundred-pound note. And to his joy, he beheld them lead their three husbands out of his house and out of his sight.

Within twenty-four hours, they had their men soberer and wiser than ever they had been in their lives before. On their freehold lands, in comfort, ease, and content, they reared up large families that were a joy and a credit to them. And they died, bequeathing to the world for a legacy the sure knowledge that although all men can be made fools as easy as kiss-your-hand, every woman can make her own man the foolishest fool of them all—and she can also, if she chooses (which, thank Heaven, she generally does) make him the wisest and happiest, most contented man on the world's ridge.

Their farms were bequeathed to their eldest sons, and again to *their* eldest after them, and so on down. Each heir in turn is nicknamed for his greatest ancestor, the Mad Man, or the Dead Man, or the Devil. And the three farms are, to this day, and ever will be, known as the Mad Man's Farm, the Dead Man's Farm, and the Devil's.

THE WONDERS
OF THE THREE DONALS

Donal O'Donnell was a farming man who did a small bit of tilling, a bit of shepherding, and a bit of trading at fairs—and he, with his wife Sorcha, lee-and-long miles from neighbors, lived in the wild mountain Gap of Barnesmor. No place was too lone for him, by reason he'd gone sour on the world and tooken a mighty dislike to all company—which drew on him a not-happy life.

There was a morning in winter when Donal got up before the screek of day and, gathering with him a couple o' score head of sheep, trudged over the hills for Brockagh Fair. But if he went, he didn't put foot across the threshold till he first cautioned Sorcha, as was usual with him, to keep her door barred and bolted, and make certain sure to allow no streelers nor strollers, vagrants nor vagabonds, to halt here for lodgings—for Donal set small store especially on this variety of gentry. Sorcha, she promised.

Now it wasn't a good morn when Donal started, and 'twas little better, but worse, it got as the day wore on; and the sleet and snow that came down in the evening would drive through a door—so sharp it was and bitter, and pelting like Paddy Whack. And it would melt the heart of a stone on the mountain for thinking of any poor homeless one abroad in Barnesmor Gap in such a blizzard.

Come *dayligone* [dusk] when Sorcha, who was doing *timerishes* [little chores] within the house and sweeping up the hearth in front of a bright fire, heard a *tindherara* [a din of hammering] upon the door, and, opening it for a glint, beheld a shivering old soul with a pack on his back. "The Blessing of God on this house and them's in it," says the figure. "I'm a poor packman, storm-stayed in the Gap, and I'd be forever obliged if you'd grant me a night's lodging."

Sorcha would raise all the objections in the world; but the night was so cruel, Sorcha so soft-hearted, and the poor drenched packman pleaded so pitiful and looked such an object, that her heart wouldn't let her shut him to the storm; so she said, "You can come and get a heat of the fire in your bones till my man Donal, who has small love for your sort, is near coming home."

The old fellow thanked her and prayed God to bless her, came in and made himself at home in the chimney corner.

Not long ensconced here was he till there came another *tind-herara* on the door; and, behold you! when Sorcha opened it, wasn't there another old codger with a pack on his back, like-wise shivering and begging shelter from the storm, and a night's lodging, for God's sake. Poor Sorcha first argued with him, but as she hadn't the heart to turn him away entirely, she finally bade him come in and get the fire in his bones till anigh Donal's homecoming. And he pushed in and made himself at home in the other chimney corner.

Lo and behold ye! not well seated was this second lad till a third *tindherara* rattled the door like it would go down, and there was a third peddler begging shelter from the elements and a night's lodging, for heaven's sake. And poor Sorcha couldn't help herself but let him step in—that he might get the heat in his bones atween then and her Donal's homecoming.

She warned the three o' them to make the most of their time, for that her man Donal heartily disliked all men—in particular, streelers and strollers—and couldn't bear them in his house, and would make scatterment of them if here he found them. Plump in front of the fire this third man settles himself; and there they sat with their packs by their sides, each man of them pipe-smoking, and same time reeking such clouds from their soaked rags that you wouldn't know most which the clouds came from—their *dudeens* (pipes) or their duds.

However, not long till comes on the door another *tindherara*, and louder and wickeder it was than any yet; and when Sorcha went and drew the bolt again, who should step in but Donal himself—far before she had any right to expect him! The look that overdarkened Donal's countenance, the instant he beheld what was planted at the fire before him, was a caution for cronies and two-year-old calves!

Says he to Sorcha, "I thought, my good woman, I warned you, before walking out the threshold this morning, to give house-room neither to streelers nor strollers—and is this how you've obeyed me?"

Poor Sorcha, she pleaded that, much as she'd like to obey him, she hadn't the heart to turn away a dog on a night like this, let alone a Christian, and that she'd only let them enter for to thaw the froze marrow in their bones atween their coming and his.

This mollified Donal but little. He'd allow the three lads, he said, just a quarter an hour to turn themselves at the fire and do the other side, afore going.

They thanked him. He pulled forward then a stool to the fire, himself, lit his pipe, and put speak upon them. He asked the first—him in the far chimney corner, what his name was, and what he was to trade.

"Donal O'Sheary by name, if it please you," says the old lad, replying, "and a peddler to trade, I am."

"And what's your name?" says Donal O'Donnell, says he, to

the old fellow in the other chimney corner, "and what your followin'?"

"Donal O'Neary by name," says he, "I am, and I follow peddlin' for a scant livin'."

"Well, well!" says Donal O'Donnell. And then, "What's your name?" says he to the man in the middle, beside himself, "and your profession?"

"Peddlin' is my profession," says he straight back, "and Donal O'Leary my name."

"Well, well, well, well!" says Donal O'Donnell, says he, "if that isn't the queerest circumstance ever I heard tell in my life, and I'm a middling old man now! Here's three peddlers of ye come, each one independent of the other, to my house in my absence; every one of ye is named Donal, and I Donal myself! If a queerer thing befell before, ever, I'd travel a *laghey* bit, and then a mile further, to shake hands on the man who met up with it."

"In troth, and," said the first old man, Donal O'Sheary, says he, "maybe it isn't so far you'd have to go for that same."

"What do you mean?" says Donal O'Donnell, says he.

"I mean to say that meself met with as queer—and maybe you'd grant queerer."

"I don't believe you," says Donal O'Donnell to his face.

"And what will you owe me if I prove you mistaken?" says Donal O'Sheary.

"The sweetest of a supper and the softest of a bed," says the man of the house.

"Good!" says Donal O'Sheary, says he. "Then hear to my story."

DONAL O'SHEARY'S STORY

"When I was a lump of a *bouchal* [lad] of nigh one-and-twenty, my father—a farmer on the banks of the Strile in Tyrone, owning as fine and flourishing a farm as any to be found between here and there—the Farm of the Fort, it was called, by reason that there was a lovely, soft, green Fairy Fort arising sheer from the holm in the farm's center; On a May Eve (day the fairies have power extraordinary) says my father to meself, 'Donal,' says he, 'take the boy-servant and the girl-servant with you by break o' day tomorrow, and start to the bog for a good day's turf-cutting, the three of ye.'

"Well and good. By break o' day, as directed, myself and the boy and girl were in the gray light facing for the bog. Taking a short cut across the fields, we were bypassing the Fairy Fort when doesn't Brigid clap sudden her hands and cry, 'Och, see the lovely wee well!' And, behold ye! sure enough there was the lovelist well eyes ever rested on, bubbling up clear and beautiful where no man had ever known a well before!

"Says Brigid, says she, stooping down on one knee, 'I'll have a sup of it for good luck,' and in the palm of her hand she lifted a moddycum to drink. 'Why wouldn't I have a sup for good luck, too,' says Rory, says he, getting down likewise.

" 'Well,' says I, 'meself'll not be behindhand if good luck's going round!' And on my benders I dropped too. We were striving who'd be the quickest to get the first drink. But when we did drink and stood up again, we beheld the strangest happening that man or mortal ever beheld in this world! Brigid was changed into a brave-looking boy, Rory transformed into a winsome young woman, and meself stood up a solemn, shaven priest. And we were in another country entirely!

"Strange and very strange as was all this, curiously it wasn't one bit strange to ourselves. I was priest of the parish that I found meself in, and me doing my duties with no wonder in the world either to meself or to any of my congregation—every soul of whom I knew as if I'd been born and bred among them. The young man and young woman that had been Brigid and Rory, they fell in love with one another without loss of time and came to me to marry them. Which I did. And they contentedly began life as parishioners of mine. A model couple they were, more by the same token—and an example to all married couples under me, so that often and often, when I was preaching of a Sunday, I held the pair up for a parable to the parish. They, like me, put in six happy years, and had half a dozen children born to them, that they were rearing up decently and well—a credit to them and to all of that countryside.

"During the same years I had my fill of work before me, managing and caring for a big, unruly parish—and lovingly I wrought at it. I christened and married hundreds, and buried scores upon scores. I was bringing on my parish wonderfully, to the delight of my bishop, who prophesied there was chance and a half of my filling his shoes when he'd be called Above. And he was an old man now.

"Well and good. At the end of this time, one day, on my way home from a sick call, I dropped in at the home of my favorite parishioners, for to find how they were coming—as often I used to do. They said I was the very man in all the world they were wishful to see. Next morning being May Eve, they were going to take a holiday to themselves—which they hadn't done in six years gone—and were driving to the Wood of the Five Oak Trees, several miles away, taking with them lashings and leavings of eatin' and drinkin' in order to spend a healthful, hearty, joyful day; and wouldn't I come with them? Right gladly I consented.

"Off we found ourselves driving in the mouth of the morn. In the heart of the wood, we built a fire and made our breakfast. After we'd eaten a hearty meal, their eldest, who'd been running around, exploring, came in with the news that he'd discovered the loveliest little fountain ever was seen, shooting high in the air and showering rainbow spray for far and wide. We went to view it; and sure enough, it was an entrancing object, a beautiful fountain that, curiously, none of us had ever heard tell of in these woods before. Their eldest little girl had fetched with her a cup, and the water was so clear, so sparkling and beautiful, she thought she'd like a drink of it. She held the cup under the falling spray till it filled, and then handed around for each of us to sample. It had the curiousest effect you ever saw; each one of us got drowsy, immediately we had sipped of it. We went and stretched out, one here, one there, one yonder, saying we'd have three winks of sleep. We hardly knew we were asleep till we woke up, and where and what did we find ourselves but three—a servant boy, servant girl, and my right self, standing at the foot of the Fairy Fort on my father's farm in Derraherk of Tyrone! I wasn't a priest at all, at all, but a farmer's son; and Rory was the young man he had been; and Brigid the same young woman! And no one of us an hour older than we had been on that morning when the first happening happened to us!

"There was never a well to be seen at the foot of the Fairy Fort; neither was there a fountain. When the three of us streeled home, my father's eyes, at sight of us, stood half a finger from his face, and he fainted cold. When he came himself, he questioned where had we been since we went from home six years ago, and how was it we all stood still at the same age as when we left. Since we went away, trace nor track of us hadn't been found, and it was concluded that all three of us had drowned in a bottomless bog hole. We were given up for lost, and Dead Masses prayed for our souls' reposing.

"My father, when he heard our story, wouldn't harbor in his house beings like us, he said, under spells; for we'd fetch him ill luck. So he turned us away, I for awhile wrought a day with this man and a day with that, till I rose the price of a pack. I bought that, put it on my back, shook my foot upon the King's highroad, and have been traveling from that day till the storm drove me to your door, Donal O'Donnell, this night.

"There's my story for you. What do you think of it, my good man?"

"I think," says Donal O'Donnell, says he, "that it's the wonderfullest tale I heard tell in my life. Sorcha," says he to his wife, "make Donal O'Sheary the best supper the house can afford, and prepare him the softest shake-down.

"And now, boys," says Donal O'Donnell, says he to the other two old men, "what do you think of these wonders you have heard? Or did any of you ever hear tell of anything to compare with them?"

"Indeed, and I did," says Donal O'Neary, says he.

"You did?" says Donal O'Donnell. "Upon my word, if you

can tell me anything near as wonderful, I'll make Sorcha provide
you a good supper—and a good night's lodging, moreover—
which I never did to streeler nor stroller in my life hitherto."

"Well and good," says Donal O'Neary, taking him at his
word. "Then I'll tell you the extraor'nary wonderful happenin'
that happened to myself and put me on the road a peddler.
When you've heard it, you'll say I've earned my reward."

"Come, then," says Donal O'Donnell, says he, "come, let us
hear it."

DONAL O'NEARY'S STORY

"Well," says Donal O'Neary, says he, "when I was a youth,
I was the son of a farmer, in the townland of Tawnawilly in
Donegal, who was famous for the raising of corn. There was no
harvest that he wouldn't put five hundred stacks of oats into
his haggard, and there was no Ware (spring) that he wouldn't
put a hundred plough horses into his fields. There was one particular harvest when he had, as usual, his stacks of corn stacked
in the haggard, thatched and roped, and we were settling ourselves down for a happy winter; when, what would you have
of it, we, of a morning, found one stack missing, and no trace
of where it went, or how it had gone. On the next morning,
behold ye! another stack was gone, and sight nor sign of one
straw of it wasn't to be seen on the countryside! And the next
morning after, still another stack was away! The extraor'nariest
transaction we ever knew of! The following night meself said I'd
sit up and watch the haggard. Of all nights of the year, it was
Hallow Eve night.

"Very good. I slipped inside a warm coat and stepped about
the haggard for the first hour or so, and then crouched under one
of the stacks till I'd snatch three winks of sleep; but I was soon
snapped out of it by feeling the stack a-tremble and hearing
above me a mortal hubbub. Up I jumped, and lo and behold! the
stack was covered with Little Men, the haggard was filled with
them, and so was the countryside, hill and dale, as far as eye
could carry on the brightest of moonlight. There couldn't be a

soul less than fifty thousand, each one pulling a stalk of corn, mounting it, same as you've seen children mount a walking stick, and saying, 'Up, up, my brave brown steed, and away with me!' swept off, steed and rider, and soon out of sight. When, shortly, there was only a single stalk left of the whole stack, I seized it, meself, mounted it, and says, as they did, 'Up, up, my brave brown steed, and away with me!' And at the tail of the multitude I shot off like a streak of lightning, a hundred mile a minute. In short time the host of us struck the Himalay' Mountains in the Eastern world, and at a word of command from the leader, a gate opened in the mountain's face, every soul of us swept within, and the gate clanged behind.

"Such a gorgeous place was within, it surpasses me to describe. There was a dining hall the length of the holm of Finn-Water, with tables that measured miles, lit by thousands uncountable of candles in gold candlesticks, and laid with dishes of all sorts of divinest eatables under the sun, and with decanters of enchanting drinkables. To the feast we sat down, and gluttoned to hearts' content; whereafter the tables were whisked away, and, to the music of a thousand pipers and a thousand fiddlers, the dance began. The beautiful Fairy Queen herself, a ravishing creature who'd took the table's head, picked meself for partner. Meself objected, saying that as it was now far in the night I ought to be heading for home, else they'd be missing me and screening the world for my finding.

" 'It's but young in the night yet,' she answered 'and there's a brave moon besides. We'll run just one reel, you and I, to show these people how it's done and cut them a copy. Thereafter we'll have a horse to take you home—one that'll not let much grass grow under his hooves while he's whirling you there.'

" 'Twasn't an easy matter to refuse the bewitching one, and I'm afeared I didn't try to overpower her with objections. All others on the floor cleared off and ranged themselves round, for to be beholding the pair of us. A purty fair dancer I always was reckoned—even if it's meself says it; but never before did I do finer or fancier stepping. And if meself was good at it, maybe it's her, the comely Queen, wasn't twice as good. The pair of us, I'll wager, was well worth walking a long mile on bare knees for to witness. To the mesmerizing of that multitude and paralyzing of pipers and fiddlers, we footed it fair and fast, for, I'm sure, little less than an hour; then finishing with a flourish that would do your heart good, we took hands and curtsied to the exclaiming crowd and retired amid clapping of hands that was deafening.

"After she'd inveigled my promise for to come again the next night, she put me in charge to a Little Man, who led me out to the mountainside, put a brave brown steed in under me that was worth a hundred pound if a penny, and told me 'twas mine to keep for coming again every time I hankered. And when I did—which he trusted would be often—then, by reason of the Queen's fancy for me, there'd certain sure be a welcome and twenty before me.

"I thanked him, and put the steed under and my spurs to him, and away through the air with us like a blast, and it wasn't many minutes till I landed plump in my father's haggard! But when I jumped from my handsome steed, meaning for to lead him to the stables, I found I was holdin' a straw!

"I was in consternation, you may be sure; but when I headed for the house, behold ye! it wasn't my father's little, low, thatched house was in it at all, at all, but a three-story mansion with a grand carriage drive to the door! A big bulldog chained close by made a dash at me, and, but for his chain, God be thanked, wasn't long enough, had quick have devoured me down to my shoe nails. When he couldn't reach me, he howled to waken a graveyard full; a window was thrown up overhead, and a man with a nightcap on his head and a gun in his hand thrust half of him out, and yelled for whatever ruffian was there to absquatulate quick and fast or he'd blow his brains out, if he had any.

"I whisked meself off as fast as I could and twice faster, and me sunk in bewilderment and feeling deranged in the head. I wandered and wondered till morning; and though I recognized every field, road, and stream, there wasn't house or hut that I knew at all, at all. Some of them were great high houses built in the steading of the purty little thatched one that ought to be in it. Others I come to which I used to call great yesterday, and found nothing but a rickle of stones, with nettles growing over and through them. I surely knew then something must be the matter with me. I lingered, fretting, till morning, and people were getting out and wending to the fields. Not a face of all the faces I met did I know. I mustered enough courage, at last, to inquire if this wasn't the land of Tawnawilly I was in, and the parties I asked stared me up and down and said, 'Yes, stranger, it is. Where do you come from?'

" 'Stranger!' says I. 'Do you not know young Donal O'Neary, son of old Donal M'or O'Neary, the warmest farmer in this townland or the next to it?' Their eyes would widen in wonder and they'd pass on, shaking their heads and whispering to one another.

"I surely believed now that my head was gone. I went into a very old kind of cabin that, it seemed to me, I should know the looks of, and there I found a very, very old man on one side of the fire, and a very, very old woman on the other side, nodding across the hearth at one another, they not less than ninety, if they were a day. I asked if either of them knew where I could find the home of Donal O'Neary of Tawnawilly. Both of them looked up at me, strange, and the old woman shook her head and said there wasn't now, nor ever was, one of that name in the townland. But the old man, he cried, 'Hold on, ye!'—'Yes,' says he, 'there *was* one of the name in this townland—once.' He turned to the old woman and says he, 'My poor old father (God rest him! he'll be dead fourscore years again' Candlemas) used to tell me, when I was a youngster, a queer story about one Donal M'or O'Neary, who died fifty years before he himself was born, and who had a son Donal, a fine, strapping young man, they said, who once went out of a Hallow Eve night to watch the corn stacks that were a-stealing from his father's haggard, and teetotally disappeared—to what art or part nobody ever knew—and no sign of him was ever seen more. His old father lived twenty years longer, a broken-hearted creature, and then went to a welcome grave. Sure, it isn't a legacy,' says he to me, 'you're going to look for from a man who's in his grave nigh two hundred years?'

"As the old fellow was telling me this story, I happened to see, fornenst me, the wizened visage of another very old man. And behold ye! wasn't it gazing in a looking-glass I was! It was my own face—a withered old man I found meself, instead of the bright young fellow I thought meself to be!

"To make a long story short, the people in Tawnawilly came to the conclusion that I was a demented poor creature, and they whispered and pitied me so much that I had to go from among them. I begged the price of a pack; for, old as I was, I wanted to earn my own living. I put it on my back and went out into the world.

"That," says he, "was a year ago, and I have been traveling and peddling since; till this night's storm blew me here for shelter—and there's my story for ye."

"Well, well, well, well!" says Donal O'Donnell, says he. "I thought Donal O'Sheary's story was wonderful, but yours is more extraor'nary still!—Sorcha, will you get this poor man the best supper this house ever saw, and the sweetest lying-down?— For you have earned it," says Donal O'Donnell, says he, to Donal O'Neary.

"Thank you," says Donal O'Neary.

"I'm sorry," says Donal O'Donnell, says he, then turning to Donal O'Leary, "to be making any distinctions; but I'm afeared, my good man, you'll have to be taking your departure, as I don't suffer streelers nor strollers to stop or stay in my house, without very special reason."

"But if I could show you very special reason," says Donal O'Leary, says he.

"Insense me," says Donal O'Donnell.

"By narrating," says he, "as wonderful a happening that happened to me as any that happened either of my namesakes— and maybe wonderfuller?"

"If you done that," says Donal O'Donnell, "you'd have the

best supper and bed my house could give—and be well deserving of them, moreover," says he.

"Well and good," says Donal O'Leary. "Then hear to me."

DONAL O'LEARY'S STORY

"When I was a young man," says he, "I was son to a farmer who owned a fine farm by the white strand of Teelin. There was a beautiful day in harvest, and my father had a *methial* of men [a group of volunteers] shearing corn. I was joined with the men myself, cutting from early morning. Tor'st twelve o'clock in the day, my father said to me, 'Donal,' says he, 'it's drawing on time your mother would be putting together the men's dinner. Step home,' says he, 'and fetch her in a *go* [any amount needed] of wather.'

"I threw down me hook and trotted home. My mother gave me a pair of water buckets, and I went, singing, to the well on the strand, for to draw the *go* of water. The water in the well, when I got to it, looked so cool and clear and enticing, that, setting down the buckets, I went upon my knees and stooped to take a sup. But doesn't I see in the water the reflection of the shore, and of the beautiful calm tide that lapped the white strand —and gliding over the tide, a lovely little boat in full sail, which, faster than you could say it, sailed right into the strand anigh me. I jumped up, and, sure enough, beheld the little boat just grating on the gravel. Down I ran, and halted, admiring it, but soon stepped inside for to get the sensation. Instant I was in, off started the boat and away with me! Westward we glided.

"It was the smoothest and delightfullest of motion—and so enchanting that I felt no bit alarmed, though I seen Teelin's strand leave my sight, next Teelin's hills, and then the great mountain of Sliabh Liag, sink away. Lo! for three days and nights I glided on, not knowing hunger nor thirst nor loneness nor fear, but every hour pleasanter and lovelier and enchantinger than the other. On the evening of the third day, a delightful green land rose over the water, and in short time we ran in on a dazzling white shore.

"A gorgeous castle with a crowd of towers to it, arose from a green knowe [knoll] above. I leaped from the boat and to the castle. The hall door wide open, I stepped inside—and found myself in a grand hall, where were dozens of the beautifullest damsels eye ever beheld, some combing long hair, others embroidering on silks, and several reclining on couches, more of them in groups chatting, and still others dancing to the most entrancing music mortal man ever hearkened to. There was one damsel, however, far beautifuler and far grander than all the rest, she, sitting upon a golden throne at the head of the hall, by thirteen of the rarest of maidens surrounded.

"She signaled for me to come to her. She set me on a silver throne beside her golden one, welcoming me to the Island of Fair Women. She discoursed me in the sweetest voice and enchantingest discourse that ever on these ears fell. Meself, I didn't know one minute from another minute, or one hour from the next, but sat in cloud of glory, harkening to her. I could have harkened, I thought, for a hundred years as easy as for an hour and been as greedy at the ending as its beginning.

"She informed me that she and her fair damsels had been long waiting and wishing for me, and that was why at length she sent the magic boat to Teelin's white strand to fetch me to her.

"I was given at night a gorgeous room and a bed where you'd sink so far out of sight in the soft down that I'd hardly know my way back to earth again when I awoke in the morning.

"I was sitting beside the Queen of the Island of Fair Women next day again, she on her gold throne and me on my silver one, the beauteous damsels there dancing, singing, and enjoying themselves in all manner of ways; and if I was in captivation the day before, her sweet discoursing this day enraptured me entirely.

"For three weeks of bliss we were wooing and at the end of that time were wedded in a wedding far grander, more dazzling than I thought even Heaven could afford. The festivities and rejoicings lasted nine days and nine nights, and the last day and night were better than the first.

"The beauty of that Island and the delights were beyond all I'd ever dreamt of, and the days went by in bliss, each one more wonderful than the last. Beautiful birds of the colors of the rainbow made music in the groves day and night; the trees drooped with the rarest of fruit, and the flowers on the dale were thick as is the heather on your mountainside. Every day the island was brighter and more beauteous than the day gone, and every hour more entrancing than the other. I knew neither cark nor care, my heart was as high and mind as gay as the lightest-hearted bird that sang in the treetops.

"Months went so; years passed so; scores of years passed so. A family of fifteen fair children grew up around us, and were married, and had children again, all fairest of the fair, from the first to the last. The strange thing was that, though many were born, no one died. All grew up to be beautiful young men and women —and halted there, no soul on the Island showed older than twenty, youth's bloom was ever on their cheeks and in their hearts.

"When I had been a hundred years here, it was like ten; but when I had lived three hundred I couldn't believe it was twenty —so filled with delight were my days.

"At the end of three hundred years, however, I one day took a longing and felt a loneliness to see Teelin's white strand once more. I told my fair bride I wanted one hour of Ireland, and she objected. But the lonesomeness and longing grew, and I begged her and beseeched, till, at long and at last, she gave in. She had the magic boat prepared. She embraced and kissed me, and handed me into it with weighty warnings. The boat should sail along the edge of Teelin's white strand, and give me a fair and full view of all that I longed to see; but, on peril of my happiness, I must not land nor let foot of me touch Ireland's earth.

"I gave faithful promise. I kissed her good-by, and off I was started, sailing fast and far. I sailed for three pleasant days and three pleasant nights, and, on a morning bright and beautiful, the boat bore in upon Teelin's fair strand, and along it coasted—till at last it came opposite our own little well upon the strand. Instantly I beheld the lovely little well, I was seized with a great longing to drink from it—a longing that was hard to resist. I remembered my promise, but then, I said, it would only just need one bare minute and no one would be the wiser. I'd speed to it, snatch three bare sups, and back again, satisfied and happy, and ready for further hundreds of unfretting years in the Island of Fair Women.

"I threw the anchor, jumped to the strand, and straight to the well with me. On my knees to it I was joyfully bending, meeting my own image in the water—when behold ye! another picture suddenly took the place of mine in the well! There was pictured the strand and the sea—and by Heaven, yes! my boat, all sails set, casting off upon the tide!

"Up sprang I—and would bound then to the tide, where, sure enough, my boat was fast gliding away. But I stumbled and fell crash over some objects—a pair of water cans that some stupid body had put right in the path. The boat was vanished when I arose. I turned to curse the cans and the fool who set them there. Then it flashed on me, 'You idiot, they're the very cans you, yourself, set down there, three hundred years ago!'

"I was dazed and driven out of myself—till sudden I heard a voice, loud and sharp, calling, 'Donal, are you going to need away all day for to fetch the *go* of water?' It was my own mother's voice! It drove me dazed. In a sort of dream, I took hold of the cans and dipping them into the well, got their full, and, like a sleep-walker, went with them up the path into our own house! Then I heard through the daze, my mother scolding, 'It's a shame for you, young fellow, taking ten minutes to fetch a *go* of water from a well a hundred yards away. You'll leave the sheavers late for their dinner!'

"When by-and-by, I came to myself and tried to tell what happened, they all thought me gone in my mind. And the more I tried to persuade them, the worse they believed me to be. At length, the very little children nicknamed me The Wanderin' Man, and things got so uncomfortable that ere a week had passed, I had to beg my father for the price of a peddler's pack. I bought it and mounted it on my back and faced the world with it.

"And peddling I've been ever since, till the storm drove me to your door this night. And there's my story."

"Well, well, well, well!" says Donal O'Donnell, says he. "I

thought what happened to meself was wonderful; I thought what happened to Donal O'Sheary more wonderful; and what happened to Donal O'Neary extraor'narier still. But the happening that happened to you, Donal O'Leary, is the dumfoundliest happening, surely, that ever in my lifetime or any other man in his lifetime ever heard tell of. And you've earned a supper for a lord and a bed for a king. Sorcha," says he, "pull down the table and put on it plates for four and suppers for fourteen—the best the house can bring up. As long as I live," says he to Donal O'Sheary, Donal O'Neary, and Donal O'Leary, "I'll never again turn from my door a streeler or a stroller."

And, on behalf of all members of their clan, they thanked him right heartily.

The night was wilder and wilder without—one of the fearsomest that ever fell in the wild Gap of Barnesmor; but they didn't heed it one bit: they had made up their minds to make a night of it. And like it was in the old, old tales, they divided the night into three parts. The first part they gave to eating and drinking to satisfaction; the second part of it they gave to story-telling and poem-reciting; and the third part they gave to sleep. A more entrancing night, Donal O'Donnell gave in, he had never met up with in all his born life afore.

When morning came and they had breakfasted heartily and well, his lodgers shook hands with and thanked Donal O'Donnell and his good woman Sorcha, shouldered their packs, and set foot upon the road again—every man facing his own way—and left Donal O'Donnell lonesome, pining and longing for Heaven to send more streelers and strollers to come soon to his door again, seeking the shelter they'd surely find.

And that's the story of The Wonders of the Three Donals.

THE THREE TASKS

THERE was a King in the East, a long time ago—a tall, dark, ugly fellow whose dearest delight was depriving of their lives the rarest heroes and noblest champions that the world knew.

In his castle was a most beautiful maiden, Fiona, whom he called daughter, but really had stolen from her home when she was a child. So famed was her loveliness, far and wide, that princes and nobles and knights from earth's ends came to woo her. And the despot made her beauty the best bait for luring the bravest and noblest to their undoing. For when any hero came to ask her hand, the base fellow bargained that to win her the comer must do any three tasks put before him—and if he failed, it lost him his life. As the tasks the evil one put before the suitor were always impossible to do, he, every time, had the delight of beheading the victim.

After the villain had thus destroyed no less than three hundred of the rarest of the world's youths, Dermod, the King of Ireland's son, one of the bravest and handsomest lads that the sun ever shone on, having heard the fame of Fiona's wonderful beauty, set out for the East, determined to win her, and glad to risk his life for it.

After a year and a day's perilous adventuring through the wilds and wastes of the world, Dermod reached the castle of the King of the East, and presenting himself to the tyrant, asked for the famed maiden's hand.

"Do you know the conditions for winning her?" asked the big fellow.

"Yes," said the brave boy, "and am glad to stake my life against any tasks you can put before me, to win such a worthy one."

"We'll see about that," says the King. "Be ready on the morrow's morn."

In the morning the King took Dermod out to the stables and showed him there the wonderful sight of seven miles of stables, and then said to Dermod, "These stables haven't been cleaned for seven years. You must have them cleaned, before night, as clean as they were the hour the first steed stood in them—either that or lose your head. I'll be back in the evening to find how you've fared. Good-bye!"

Poor Dermod, he looked at his task dumfounded. No mortal could accomplish it!

But he was a brave fellow. Do or die, he took hold of a *graip* [a pitchfork] and started to graip out the mountainous piles before him. But lo and behold! the first graipful he flung out, fifty graipfuls came flying in! And next graipful he flung out, fifty graipfuls came flying in! And the same with the next and the next. And if he wrought from that day to Doomsday, he'd still keep 'larging the piles instead of lowering them.

Tired out and despairful, at last he sat down on a stump outside, his head in his hands, and he lamenting sore.

He found a gentle hand laid on his shoulder, and looking up, beheld the most enchanting vision his eyes ever rested on. There stood the beautiful maiden herself, smiling upon him—her face and her smile were so radiant that they brightened and lightened the heart of him, and his woe and his worry were ended, no matter what should happen to him thereafter.

"I see you haven't won far with your work, brave boy," Fiona said.

"No," said Dermod. "I have failed and tonight will lose my head. But that will be small loss compared with failing my chance of winning such a beautiful maiden as you!"

Fiona smiled again her captivating smile and said, "Your chance isn't lost yet, my brave Prince." And taking from her pocket a little silver graip, she dug it in the first heap within. Immediately, the little graip began working of itself—it flung out a graipful and lo! ten thousand graipfuls went with it! It flung out another graipful and lo! ten thousand more graipfuls went with it! And then another, and another, the same. Till in short time the seven miles of stables were as clean as the hour that the first steed stood there. And Dermod, past himself with delight and gratitude, on his knees thanked Fiona from the bottom of his heart. "I want no thanks, my noble Prince," said she. "I like you so, that it's only joy to serve you. But," she said, "be sure you don't breathe a word to the Dark Man that you got aid from me, else my life would be forfeit as well as yours."

Dermod vowed that carthorses wouldn't draw the secret from him. And she hurried off. Dermod put his hands in his pockets and went whistling and singing around and about till evening came. And with it came the King, smiling all over, for he was sure of his prey.

"Well, how have you come along?" he asked lightly.

"Oh, moderately well," says Dermod. "Have a glance within for yourself."

And when the King glanced into the stable and saw what he saw, he grew black in the face with venom. "You eternal vagabond!" he stormed at Dermod. "How did you a task that was impossible to mortal man to do?"

Said Dermod lightly, "It surely was a hardy enough task— but not too much for a healthy lad from Ireland. Even if you'd made it a bit harder, I think I could have managed without overstraining myself."

The Dark Fellow was amazed. "But never mind," says he. "That's only your first task put behind you. Tomorrow you'll face one that will defy you to begin, let alone finish."

Said Dermod, pretending to be careless, though he was far from it inside of him, "I have a habit of letting every morrow worry for its own woe."

"Very well," says the King. "We'll see."

Well and good. Next morn, after breakfast, the King ordered Dermod to come along with him. He led Dermod to the stables once more. "These stables," said he, "sorely need new thatching. Your task today is to thatch all seven miles of them—and to do the job, not with straw, but thatch them with the feathers of the birds of the air, and have no two feathers the same, or from the same bird. That little job you're to finish before night or lose your head." And he went away.

Dermod, thunderstruck, gazed at the seven miles of roof, which, before night, must be thatched with the feathers of the birds of the air, and no two feathers the same, or from the same bird—or lose his head. His heart fell. But he was a brave fellow, and when his senses returned to him, he started after every bird he saw, helter-skelter, this way, that way, up and down, over and back—till he'd put in three hours of it and was ready to drop in his tracks. He had accumulated three feathers that he looked at in the heart of his hand! Down he dropped on a convenient stump, burying his head in his hands, lamenting sore. All at once he found a gentle hand laid on his shoulders, and a voice sweeter than anything else in the world, saying, "Dermod, brave fellow, I see you haven't won far with your work today!"

He looked up and beheld the same rare vision as dawned on his sight the day before.

"No," said Dermod. "I have failed and tonight will lose my head. But that will be small loss compared with failing my chance of winning such a beautiful maiden as you."

Fiona smiled again her captivating smile and said, "Your chance isn't lost yet, my brave Prince."

She took from her pocket a little golden whistle, and blew on it three times. Instantly, from the four corners of the world, the world's birds came sweeping till they shut out the skies overhead—began flying hither and thither over the stables, each bird from its wing dropping on the roof a feather, one feather falling on another—and another—and another—till in time, as short almost as it takes to tell it, the seven miles of stables were thatched with the feathers of the world's birds, and no two feathers the same, nor of the same bird. And Dermod, past himself with delight and gratitude, on his knees thanked Fiona from the bottom of his heart.

"I want no thanks, my noble Prince," said she. "I like you so much that it's only joy to serve you. But," she added, "be sure you don't breathe a word to the Dark Man that you got aid from me, or else my life will be forfeit as well as yours."

Dermod vowed that carthorses wouldn't draw the secret from him. And when she hurried off, Dermod put his hands in his pockets and went whistling and singing around and about till evening came.

In the evening, into the yard comes the King, smiling all over, feeling certain he'd have Dermod's head this time. But lo! when he glanced up, he beheld the seven miles of roof, all thatched with the feathers of the birds of the air and no two feathers the same or from the same bird! He put out of him a thunderous shout and went black with rage. "You eternal rogue and rascal!" he stormed at Dermod. "Tell me how you did such a task that I believed impossible to mortal man."

"Oh," said Dermod lightly, "it surely wasn't dead easy—but still not too hard for a healthy lad from Ireland. If you had even made it a bit harder still, I think I could have managed without overstraining myself."

"Never mind," the fellow rasped out. "That's only your second task put behind you. Tomorrow you'll face one that will defy you to start, let alone finish."

Said Dermod, pretending to be careless, though he was far from it inside, "I have a habit of letting every morrow worry over its own woe."

"Very well," says the King. "We'll see."

Well and good. Next morn, after breakfast, he took Dermod down the lawn in front of the castle—to a pond that had an island in the center; and on the island was one tree whose top all but touched the sky—ten times taller than any tree Dermod had ever seen before. Its trunk, from earth to sky, sprouted neither branch nor bud, but was smooth and shiny as a spear. Only at its top a few branches grew from it.

Said the King, "That tree is three hundred yards high. It is so smooth and slippery that no man ever got grip to climb one yard. At its top is a crow's nest with three eggs. I want you to have those eggs here for me this evening, or lose your head."

A dazed and dumfounded man was Dermod, standing transfixed, gazing up that tree—and grief got hold of him! Still he was brave, and when he came to himself, he went at the tree, determined. But when he spread arms round the tree to climb, he found it so slippery that every time he'd manage to pull himself up a yard, he'd immediately slither back to the bottom again. For long and long he kept trying and failing—till at length the last little bit of strength left his body, and he collapsed at the tree's foot, his face buried in the ground, and he lamenting sore.

Just then he found a hand on his shoulder, and a voice sweeter than anything else in the world, saying, "Dermod, brave fellow, I see you haven't gained with your work."

"No," said Dermod, "I have failed and tonight will lose my head. But that will be small loss compared with the thought of losing you!"

Fiona smiled again her entrancing smile and said, "Your chance isn't lost yet, my brave Prince. Maybe I can help you."

"No, no, no!" Dermod said. "No, my sweet girl. You cannot help me this time. You might clean out the stables for me, and thatch them too with feathers, but this is one task beyond yours or any other power on earth to do."

"We'll see about that," says she.

She stooped, and to Dermod's amazement began picking the bones out of her lovely bare foot—picking, picking, and picking till she had picked out three hundred! She showed him how, putting one against the tree trunk, it stuck there and made a step, another a yard higher on the trunk made another step, and so on—gave him the bones to place for himself, and have a ladder all the three hundred-yard journey to the crow's nest at the top. "Be very sure," she warned him, "coming down again, to pick and take every single bone with you. I have no powers," she said, "to use them twice for the same thing. The King washes my feet before I go to bed nightly. If he found a bone missing, he would discover that I, by my magic, was doing your tasks, and my life would be lost then, also."

Dermod said he'd forget his own head before he'd forget a single bone of her precious foot. Making a ladder as he went, he mounted the tree, got the eggs in his pocket and down with him again, gathering the bones as he came. On the earth again, happy, he handed the bones, with his heart's gratitude, to Fiona, who, when she would put the bones back where they belonged, found, lo and behold, the top joint of her little toe was missing! He'd left it at the top of the tree!

Dermod was overcome with shame and grief. "Are you now lost," says he, "my dear lovely one? That myself's lost doesn't matter."

She thought for a minute—then said, "We have one chance for our lives."

Then she told him how, after the Dark Fellow's eating a great meal every night, he slept for an hour in his chair, and when he awoke, called her from her room for the foot-washing. "Now, when he sleeps tonight," she said, "you must carry me off on the swiftest steed in the stable. When you go to the stable, you'll meet first on entering, a row of three hundred and sixty-five black steeds. You'll pass them without regard. Next you'll meet a row of three hundred and sixty-five chestnuts. Don't regard them either. Next and last, you'll come to a row of three hundred and sixty-five white steeds. But don't take the first in the row, nor the second, nor the third—pass on till you come to the three hundred and sixty-fifth. That's the jewel and gem of all steeds in the stable and in the world. Saddle and bridle and lead it to my window, when I'll slip out and mount before you—and off for our lives. The Dark Fellow would be on our heels in an hour, and our swift steed weighted down with two, he'd have every chance to overtake us, but I'll work some magic that will double our start of him. We'll maybe escape."

And so their attempt to escape was planned and agreed to.

In a mad, boiling rage was the King when he came that evening and discovered the third and last task performed—but when he could speak sensibly, he said to Dermod, "We'll see more about this business in the morning."

"Yes, we'll see," says Dermod.

Sure enough, the instant the King fell asleep that night and she heard his first snore, Fiona in her room, ready for departure, put her magic on an apple and dividing it in quarters, laid one quarter at her washstand, another at her dressing table, one at her room door, and the fourth in the corridor—ere she stepped out and mounted before Dermod—upon a beautiful white mare, swiftest of all the steeds in the stable. Then away like the wind with them both!

When the bad man awaked, he called for Fiona, for her foot-washing. "Are you ready, Fiona?" The apple-quarter at the washstand answered, "I'm just washing my hands." After some time he called again, and the apple-quarter at the dressing table answered, "I'm combing my hair." And when he called again later, the piece at her room door answered, "I'm just leaving my room." And at a fourth, wild, angry, later calling, the last quarter answered, "I'm coming along the passage." When finally he screamed, "Are you coming or must I go drag you here by the hair of the head?" there came back to him only the sound of silence! Then he madly rushed to Fiona's room, found her gone, and guessed what had happened. Out with him to the stable, mounted the swiftest horse he could find, and away like the wind after— But Fiona's plan had given Dermod and herself another hour.

They were overtaking the wind before and putting it behind, all through the night, and at day's breaking were rejoicing themselves that they were saved, when they heard a thundering of hooves—and Dermod, looking back beheld the Dark Fellow on his steed not a quarter mile behind and gaining at every bound!

"We're lost!" cried Dermod. "He's coming after and overtaking us!"

"Not lost yet," answered Fiona. "Put your hand in the mare's left ear and tell me what you find."

Dermod did as he was bid, and, "I find a chip of wood," says he.

"Fling it over your left shoulder," says Fiona.

Dermod did so, and behold! a great wood sprang up behind—between them and the Dark Fellow.

They rode before the wind all that day and were slacking at falling of night, sure that now they were safe, when, hearing again the thundering of hooves, Dermod looked back and beheld their pursuer sweeping after and gaining at every bound. Again Dermod cried, "We're lost! Here he comes, and overtaking us fast!"

"We're not lost yet," answered Fiona. "Look in the mare's right ear and tell me what you find there."

"A wee pebble is in it," says Dermod.

"Throw it over your right shoulder and see what will happen," said Fiona.

Dermod threw the pebble over his right shoulder—and behold! a great, high, rugged, rocky mountain was behind them, shutting off their pursuer.

All night they were going before the wind again, and by the morn's first light began to slack, certain they were safe, when, sudden, they were deafened by great hoof-beats behind—and looking back, Dermod nearly became paralyzed. There was the Fellow now, thundering at their heels, not fifty yards away, waving a drawn sword above him as he gained at every bound!

"We're lost for good!" cried Dermod. "He's on top of us with a drawn sword!"

"Quick! Quick!" cried Fiona. "Look between the mare's ears, and throw over your head what you find there!"

Between the mare's ears Dermod found a drop of pitch—which, when he threw it back overhead, set a river of roaring, boiling, pitch rolling behind—between them and the Dark Fellow—who was coming with such raging force that he and his steed plunged into the boiling flood and sank out of sight, never to rise more!

Safe Dermod and Fiona were now, and joyous. And joyously they rode on till they reached Ireland, and reached his father's castle—where there was tremendous welcome for him whom they thought lost—and for this marvelously beautiful maid he had brought with him.

Dermod and Fiona were wedded in the greatest, gladdest, most gorgeous wedding Ireland ever witnessed before or since. The King and Queen—Dermod's father and mother—resigned from their thrones and had the new King and Queen crowned in their stead. The revelling and rejoicing lasted a year and a day, whilst the hearts of Dermod and Fiona were high with happiness. And through a long, long and blissful reign, they were never less happy.

And the good Lord grant that all of your days, yours and mine, be as bright and blissful as were theirs.

THE BOLD HEROES OF

HUNGRY HILL

HUNGRY Hill was the sad site that Jack and his bold heroes hailed from. And sure enough 'twas well named, for a hungrier patch there wasn't again on Ireland's ground. Jack, he was bred there, born and reared. When he was sixteen, one May morning, and found his own and his widowed mother's winter supply was nigh eaten out, he considered it time that he was up, and out in the world, and doing for himself. So he asked his mother to bake him a cake and give him her blessing, and he would off with him to push his fortune till the harvest came in with fresh supply for both in their little cabin.

Right enough, his mother baked Jack a cake and put it in his pocket, gave him her blessing and bade him good-bye. And out the brave lad went off with him to face the world for four months to come.

Well and good, Jack hadn't traveled far till he met a poor man who begged for something to eat. "Well," said Jack, "I have a cake here for myself, but I had a right hearty breakfast this morning, I'm afraid from the looks of you, is more than you've had for a month. You're more in need of it than I, so here it is, with a heart and a half."

"My blessing on you," said the poor man. "And may God's blessing never be far from you wherever you go."

Jack thanked him heartily and fared forward.

He hadn't traveled far till he came upon an old man unmercifully beating an ass. Jack took the stick and beat the man with it and drove him off. The ass thanked Jack right heartily and said the old man wasn't his owner anyhow, but had stolen him a month ago and seldom stopped beating him since.

"Well, I'm glad I relieved you," said Jack.

"Is it any harm," ventured the ass, "to ask where you're going?"

"No harm in the wide world," said Jack. "I'm off to push my fortune till the harvest comes in."

"Of all things in the world, I'd like to travel with you," said the ass.

"The more the merrier," said Jack. "Pack your belongings and join."

The ass threw over his shoulder a bag of grass that his master had pulled for him and came limping along with Jack.

Not far had they fared when they heard coming toward them a clang-bang that would waken the twelvemonths' dead, and there came tearing over the next hilltop a spotted dog with more tins tied to his tail than would furnish half the houses in the countryside—the mischief of bad boys in the glen beyond. As the poor animal would cross their track, Jack stopped him and untied from his tail the menagerie of tins that was torturing him.

"Heaven bless you, Jack, for the glorious release," said the dog.

"You're welcome, indeed, my poor fellow," said Jack.

"Is it any harm, Jack," said the dog, "to ask where you're going in the morn?"

"No harm in the wide world," said Jack. "It's off I am to push my fortune till the harvest comes in."

"There's nothing in the wide world I'd like better than to join you," said the dog, "if it's compliable with you."

"The more the merrier," said Jack. "Pack your belongings and join the bold brigade."

The dog threw over his shoulder, on a string, a pig's foot he had been chewing when the bad boys happened. And Jack and the ass and the dog trudged on.

Not far had the bold heroes traveled till they met up with a cat whose left forefoot was caught in a rabbit trap, and it was crying most piteously. In quick time Jack had the poor thing released, and its foot bound in a bandage that he tore from his shirt. The cat thanked Jack right heartily and then said, "Is it any harm to ask where you're going, yourself and your bold heroes?"

"No harm in the wide world," said Jack. "I'm off to push my fortune till the harvest comes in, and these bold heroes have volunteered as my bodyguard."

"There's nothing in the wide world I'd like better than to join the brave company," said the cat, "if no one considers it objectionable."

"The more the merrier," said Jack. "Pack your belongings and join."

The cat threw over its shoulder a mouse it had caught before stumbling into the trap, and forth the bold company fared.

Not far had they gone till they came upon a cock meandering up and down and crowing and crowing and crowing most desperately.

"What's the matter with you, my bully boy?" said Jack, when they came up to him, "that ye're raising a hullabaloo would frighten the Man in the Moon!"

"Oh," said the cock, said he, "I'm lost! I'm lost! Yesterday morning I foolishly left the home that I'd never lost sight of before, for I thought I wanted to see the world—and now I don't know where I am. Can you tell me?"

"I can that," said Jack. "You're where you're standing."

"Am I?" said the cock. "I didn't know, for I have no learning."

"You're only a trifle confused," said Jack.

"I'm all comflusthered," said the cock, "and don't know whether it's on my head or my heels I am."

"You're on your heels, right enough," said Jack.

"Thanky for that," said the cock. "And is it any harm to ask where yourself and your bold heroes are going?"

"No harm in the wide world," said Jack. "I'm off to push my fortune till the harvest comes in, and these brave fellows have volunteered as my bodyguard."

"There's nothing in the wide world I'd like better than to join ye," says the cock, "if there's no objection."

"The more the merrier," said Jack. "Pack your belongings and come."

The cock threw over his shoulder, in a sack, three grains of corn he'd saved for his supper, and with his new comrades marched forth.

Very well and good, then; Jack and the ass and the dog and the cat and the cock fared forth, and they traveled all that day until the night was coming down. Then they cast an eye around them, and fixed on a little house under a hill, which Jack said looked likely for a lodging. And when they came near, they saw the man of the house, himself, sitting out by a ditch, and he looking gloomier and more dire than the night that was over him.

"God save you, sir," said Jack.

"God save yourself and your company," the man replied. "May I ask who you are, or where you're headed for?"

"You may, and welcome," said Jack. "We're a regiment of bold heroes from Hungry Hill faring forth to push our fortune till the harvest comes in, and we'll be forever obliged to you if you'll let us put up with you for the night."

"Ha! Ha! Ha! Ha!" laughed the man, with a bitter bit of a laugh. "You'd all be hearty welcome, indeed, if the house was my own."

"And isn't it your own?" asked Jack.

"Well, it is, and it isn't," said the man. "It ought to be me own, and always is me own, excepting for the four summer months from May Day till September morning. On May Day of every year a regiment of me wife's relatives, headed by her grumpy old grandmother, come in and camp on top of us for the summer; and then, the only peace or ease I know is when I

come out to sit by the ditch here, with my own black thoughts for company. My wife is badly put out, too, but because they're her own kith, she wouldn't say a bad word to them; and I'd never hear the last of it from her if myself raised my voice above my breath, exceptioning. The pack came in this very day," he said, "and now my torture's started."

"I'm right heartily sorry for you," said Jack, "and I speak for my company as well as myself. Get us off your mind, for we'll be moving on and searching elsewhere."

"No! No! No!" said the man, said he. "The old grandmother and her confederates are in bed, sound asleep, for they're tired as dray horses from their journey. I have a big empty kitchen, and as I never yet turned wanderer from my door, you'll go no step farther. If it pleases you, all five of you may make yourselves at home with me till daylight begins its dawning. But you'll have to get out at the streak of day, before the old grandmother begins her day's padrollin'."

Jack thanked him and promised they'd do as he directed.

And, in the big kitchen they disposed themselves, the ass to sleep in one corner, Jack to snore in another, the dog taking his snooze inside the kitchen door, the cat curled in front of the fire, and the cock on a bar high up above the kitchen's middle.

That would have been well and good, only in the stream of the night the old grandmother waked with a sting of hunger in the stomach, got up, and streaked to the kitchen for a bite of something to bribe the craving. And lo! and behold you, the first step she put in the kitchen door, she stepped on the dog, who put out of him a howl that was heard on the Cape o' Good Hope, and sank his biters in the calf of her leg. The old hussy gave a howl and two jumps, landing on the cat, who put out of her a screech that sounded in Siberia, and she made a leap at the old lady's unoccupied calf. The cock, aroused and frightened, lit down on the old lady's head, digging his claws in her skull and whanging both sides of her face with his wings, making her screech and

The cock, aroused and frightened, lit down on the old lady's head, digging his claws into her skull and making her screech and yell.

yell and back against the ass's tail, who, thereupon lifted both heels and gave her such a *sullander* behind as shot her like a cannon ball through the kitchen door and flat on her face without.

When she'd struggled to her feet, she met her gang of confederates rushing from their rooms to find it 'twas the End of the World.

"Go back!" she shouted. "Go back with ye one and all. Clap on your clothes, pack your things, and abscond from under the roof of people who have no more respect for their kindred than to lodge them in a lunatic asylum with a menagerie of devilish beasts and birds! Don't let the sun rise on ye within sight of this plague hole, nor ever one of you darken these doors again!"

In an hour's time, the old termagant, with her regiment of relatives and all their belongings, had disappeared.

There was no more sleep there that night, for the man, and indeed, his wife, too, were joyed out of their senses, and their hearts hoisted to heaven with relief. There was nothing too good in the house, then, for Jack and his bold heroes, and all of them ate, drank, sang, and made jollification till morning. And for a fortnight Jack and his company were there, fondled and feasted, and only by main force could they tear themselves away then from the happy people, who wanted to hold them for a year and a day.

Well and good, Jack and his company quitted that place and fared forth again, traveling before them till it was near to nightfall. Then, seeing a likely house for lodging, they drew on it and knocked on the door, but got no answer. They went round the house and round the house, gleeked in every window, and learnt it was deserted. And, as they would fare farther to look for a likely lodging, a man, coming at the yard gate, asked who they were and what they wanted. And Jack told him his story, and said that he had thought he might find lodging there for the night.

Said the man, "And that you would, with a heart and a half, if I had my way and was in my own house. But," he said, "myself and my wife and little family were thrown out of this house, which is our own, by a bloodsucker to whom I was in debt five pounds. I'd have paid him when the harvest came round, but he coveted my house, which is worth five hundred, and by means of lawless law he took it and threw myself and little ones in the ditch there beyond, underneath a few sticks and a few sods we put over us to keep the weather away."

"He hasn't come to live in it yet?" asked Jack.

"No," said the man, "because my friends, to frighten him, put out the rumor that the house is haunted, and he's waiting to find for sure."

"Well," said Jack, "haunted or enchanted, if we have your good will to it, and you lift a window to let us in, we'll take our rest there anyway, and give you our hearty thanks, and blessings for your charity."

"I don't care," said the man, "if all the country lodged in it. You're welcome; and here's a window you can get in by—and get out again before the old curmudgeon finds you in the morning, and jails ye for trespassing."

With gratitude to the good man, in of the window they all got, and Jack, searching the house, found that the big parlor was the cosiest and snuggest to pass the night in. He got plenty of turf and sticks and built in its grate a bonfire that warmed the cockles o' the hearts of the world's wanderers and gave them happy hours, sitting around it till midnight and beyond. Jack had pulled the blinds on the windows for safety's sake, but nevertheless the great fire illuminated the blinds, and some frightened one carried word to the old bloodsucker that his haunted house was lit up; and he, not believing, came to see for himself, for the old fellow was a disbeliever in God, ghost, or devil—in everything except gold; and even when he came and saw the lighted windows, he cursed the countryside for cowards and said he would show them what it was to be a man! He'd face and find out what it was, and end the blather about his house being haunted. He got hold of a big pole and with it he began to batter in the house's nailed-up door.

When he heard the hurly-burly without, Jack jumped to his feet and cried to his troops, "My bully boys, there's an invasion on! Every man to his post, and every soul do his duty—Fall in!"

He planted the ass with his tail to the fire and his front paws on the parlor table, facing the door. He pulled from above the fireplace and clapped on his own head a bullock's scalp complete with the horns; then mounted the ass's back and lay along its neck, with his head above the ass's head. He mounted the dog to lie along his shoulders, the dog's head above his own. The cat was on the dog's shoulders, with her head above the dog's, and the cock on the shoulders of the cat, his head and red comb crowning the edifice.

The old fellow by now had hammered his way inside, and was pulling at the parlor door when Jack sang out to his heroes, "Now, bully boys, all together, and give the invader his welcome."

And the instant the man pushed his head in the parlor, they all of them opened their throats and let go—the ass braying, Jack yelling, the dog howling, the cat screeching, and the cock crowing, "Cock-a-doodle doo-oo-oo-oo!," in a chorus that rattled the stars in the sky. At the bewildering reception, the old fellow staggered back, his knees buckled under, and he dropped! But next minute he was on his feet again and was out of the house with a leap and a bound—and, putting a screech out of him that blasted the crows out of the trees, he was streaking across the country, his feet touching the ground only here and there. And neither himself nor any other man knew how far he fared before he fell—as good as dead.

But with the first streak of day he was back to rouse out of his sleep with his hullabaloos the poor fellow whom he had evicted, begging and imploring him to take back his haunted house and any time within five years from now pay him the five pounds he owed!

That happy poor man and his wife wanted Jack and his comrades to live and die with them. But Jack, after they got a good breakfast, thanked him right heartily and said he was sorry, but he must face the world and push his fortune till the harvest came in. So himself and his bold heroes fared forth again.

As they went ahead, said Jack, said he, "My bully boys, we're working wonders, sure enough, but so far we're accumulating no big fortune."

"The luck's before us," said the dog.

"Amen!" said the ass.

"Them's my sentiments, too," said the cat.

And the cock, to show his approval, sang out, "Cock-a-doodle-doo-oo-oo-oo!"

They pushed forward all day, and when night came down had reached a part of the country where there seemed to be no human habitation; but at last they lit upon a little hut in a wood that looked deserted, and though it had two doorways, one back, and one front, and two windowways, one at either side, there was neither door nor window on them. As it was no cheery place and was small, the animals said they would sooner sleep on the soft grass in a clump of bushes by the house, but it would be more in order for Jack, being of mankind, to lie him down within the structure. Very well; Jack made them all snug and comfortable, the animals on a soft bed of grass under the bushes and the cock roosting on a branch above them, while he went in and climbed a bit of a ladder to a half-loft that came halfways over its one room, and pulled up after him the ladder for safety.

The half-loft had nothing on it excepting odds and ends, among which was an old blunderbuss that hadn't tasted powder for fifty years and was ready to fall apart. Jack pulled it to him, for guarding, and pulled to him also a bag of chaff that he lay on —and was soon in a sound sleep.

Behold ye! in the middle of the night he was awakened with the tramp of feet and voices of men. Peeping over the edge of his loft, he saw four beardy men with lanterns, entering. They hung up their lanterns, and each man, from off his shoulder, dropped upon the table a clinking bag. They drew up four rickety chairs, sat down, and emptied out of their bags onto the table four heaps of shining gold guineas! Which made Jack's eyes start so that he believed they'd leap out of their sockets!

As they began to count their gold, one of them said, "Well, thanks be to heaven, that was an easier job than we expected."

"It would not have been no easy job," said another, "if we hadn't had the steward with us."

"He may thank heaven," said a third, "he got his fat haul of the swag."

"I don't begrudge it to him," said the fourth. "The man who'd help us plunder his own master, the owner of Castle Eskey, well deserved one bag out of five. May it prosper with him."

Jack waited for no more. He let himself out of the hole in the gable that was a window to the loft. He wakened the brigade, told them what was happening, and gave them their instructions. With no more noise than a mouse, he stationed the four of them at their posts outside the two doors and two windows, there to wait their commander's orders. Then he climbed back to his lookout post on the half-loft again—and waited his time.

When the robbers finished counting, and were in high good humor, laughing, and shouting, and singing, and drinking one another's health, and the health of the false steward of Castle Eskey, and their fun was at its height, down on their table dropped a big bag of chaff, a whistle tore the air above them, and a fearsome voice of command called out, "My bully boys, surround the house and see that no traitor escapes alive!"

"The soldiers! The soldiers! The soldiers are on us!" shouted the robbers, every man jumping to his feet and making dash for door and window! The robber who made the first window got full in his face such a wild donkey bray that he fell broad on his back in the room again. The man who made for a door had a mad dog pounce upon him with a yell, and he, putting out of himself a yell of his own, fell back likewise—with the dog atop of him. The next man was met by a screeching wild cat that crashed him to the floor, took its seat on his chest, and began clawing his eyes out. The fourth man was met by a screeching cock that stuck its claws in his head and battered him with its wings till he sank on the floor also—on his chest, crowing, the cock perched, "Cock-a-doodle-doo-oo-oo-oo!"

And when the scoundrels got back their senses, they beheld a man standing over them with a terrible big blunderbuss, ready to blow out their brains—they called out, "Mercy! Mercy! Mercy! Won't you have mercy upon us!"

"My bully boys," Jack commanded his comrades, "let the rascals up and guard them well—though there's small fear of them escaping before the muzzle of this bloody blunderbuss of mine, jammed and crammed as it is with powder and ball and various other condiments."

He made each robber shoulder a bag of the gold and started the cavalcade off for Castle Eskey—the donkey pioneering the way, the cock and the cat marching at one side, the dog at the other, and Jack presenting his blunderbuss behind.

A glad man, as you may well suppose, was the master of Castle Eskey, when, after being roused out of his bed, he received the crowd, heard Jack's story, and got his four bags of gold. And a sad man, as you may well believe, was the steward, when he was roused out of his bed, and, with the bag of gold that was found under his bed, taken down to the company in the parlor and confronted with his crime.

The five criminals were condemned to be hung, which was too good for them. "And now," said the master of Castle Eskey, "that I'm in need of a new steward, I couldn't, if I searched the world, find a better or a braver or a gallanter or more trustworthy than you, Jack. I ask you to do me the honor of being my steward for life. And with rascals roaming the country like these four men, I need brave guards for my castle, and as I couldn't find better or braver than your four comrades; my protectors I beg them to be, for their lifetime, too."

Jack sent for his old mother and brought her there to live, and she was as overjoyed with Jack's great good fortune as he was himself. One year didn't pass till the beautiful daughter of the master of Castle Eskey fell in love with Jack—for he was as handsome as he was gallant and good—and they were married before a brilliant company. Jack's four comrades stood up with him at the wedding and were admired by high and low alike. And happy as Jack and themselves were that day, they never knew one day less happy during all of their lives after.

THE DAY

OF THE SCHOLARS

'Tis a lee and long while now since the days of Feargal the Scholar; and the man who lived then hasn't had a toothache for a thousand years. In those days the great scholars of Ireland were known and noted to the world's far corners; and these notorious ones, after they had learned everything there was to learn in the world, grew so proud of their own greatness that they went traveling among one another, and east and west as well, challenging everybody to meet them in learned contests—the craziest they could think of. And the population caught the craziness, too, for whenever or wherever one of these extraordinary contests came off, the doctor would leave his patient before he had him dead, the groom would leave the bride before he had kissed her, the sentry his post, though he saw an invading army coming, and the king his crown, and the beggar his bag—every last one of them breaking his neck to see who'd be on the battleground first. So mad, at last, did the whole land become over these intellectual wrestlings that the country was going to pot, out and out, neither child nor chief caring what happened, so long as they found fools to argue with them which scholar of all Ireland was greatest and most renowned.

When the rage had reached its height, the scholars surrounded with such fame as had never been known before, and the country looking ruination in the face, a scholar of scholars, who was named above all others, Feargal the Scholar—who, after he had learned the last thing that was to be learnt in Ireland, visited every college in Europe and Asia, challenging the greatest philosophers of them, coming out victorious, and adding something new to his knowledge in every fresh country he invaded—came back to Ireland, all the world ringing with his name and fame—and came to his own native Kingdom of Kerry.

Every scholar in Ireland trembled like a windlestraw when they heard of his coming.

Feargal didn't eat a pick nor close an eye, after landing in Kerry, till he sent challenge to the High King of Ireland at Tara, for the greatest of the great scholars that the King always maintained in droves round his court to meet him in a final contest for the world's championship—a contest in which not a spoken word was to be permitted—only sign language. He named a day and date when he would appear at Tara to give it choice of fame or shame eternal.

Now the High King at Tara at this time was a man of such common sense that there was no telling what minute his scholars would raise the nation against him, and uncrown him in disgrace; and when he'd get up in the morning he'd feel for his head the first thing—to find if they'd still left it there. When he got this challenge from Feargal the Scholar, he was—inside of himself—the maddest man his kingdom knew. All of his court, though, were full of rejoicement—except the scholars. The King's scholars were the talk of the world, for they had beaten and vanquished everything that came before them up to this. They now, however, knew that there was no standing up to Feargal the Scholar, who had overcome Europe and would surely shame and disgrace them forevermore.

The nearer drew the day Feargal had named for the big contest, the pitifuller grew the plight of the King's scholars, and heart-breaking was their woe and wailing. At last, in a crowd they trooped to the King and begged that he would invent some way of saving them and saving his Court from disgrace in the face of the world.

And, in troth—for their plight would melt the heart of a mill-stone—the King was touched for them and, though he hated to do it, thought he should help them.

Now the King had heard tell, at various times, of a mighty knowledgeable little black-haired, black-whiskered man they called Dark Patrick, who lived among the hills of Donegal, and who, though he had never in his life seen the inside of a college nor glimpsed between a book's covers, was known far and wide for his extraordinary common sense—a man who, though he had unraveled many a wonderful snarl when need called him, was still as humble as he was poor, and lived quiet and peaceful in his own little hut, tilling his little patch, and desiring nothing rarer than the respect of his neighbors—all of them as poor as himself.

The King sent a courier to Donegal to fetch Dark Patrick to the palace at Tara. And to him the King gave in his case, asking what Patrick could do to aid or extricate them.

Dark Patrick, he shook his head. "I don't know," he said. "This learning is a wonderful thing. But I'll do my best to aid your friends, and the best can do no more."

"That's so," says the King.

Dark Patrick set about making inquiries if there was at the King's Court a man who had never learned to know B from a bull's foot. And everyone agreed that Johnny-One-Eye, the apple huckster's son, was not only the ignorantest man at court, but you might drag Ireland with a herring net and not find an ignoranter.

"Then," Patrick proclaimed, "Johnny-One-Eye we'll put up to overthrow Feargal the Scholar."

The great learned ones arose in uproar at this, and asked the King was he going to let this country clown, Dark Patrick from

Donegal, bring eternal disgrace upon him, and them, and the nation.

Says Patrick, "My lord, maybe some of the learned gentlemen themselves is willing to undertake the meeting and defeating of Feargal. If so, then your good name is saved and you have no use for ignorant me, so I'll be bidding you good morning and pushing for the North again."

He looked all round the great scholars to detect which of them was going to offer to meet Feargal. But one scholar looked at the other, and the other looked at the next; and the heart of every man o' them sank into his shoes, and there wasn't a soul among them would look the King in the face and say, "I'll meet Feargal."

"Then," says the King, "when no soul of you will undertake to meet Feargal, ye haven't any right to hinder this good man from whatsoever arrangement it pleases him to make."

Well and good. The great Feargal himself arrived, at last, with a retinue of all the scholars of Kerry in his train, and he'd scarce bow to the King, himself, so great and proud was he. He swept into the grand hall that had been cleared for the contest—him and his flock of shining scholars—and he seated himself on a throne on one side of the platform in view of the multitude—the scholars and the nobles and the great men who now filled the place to bursting. He called for the champion who was to contest with him.

Though the King's scholars were black in the face from madness, there were thousands there who had to stuff the tails of their coats in their mouths to block the laughing when they saw Johnny-One-Eye, in a professor's rig-out, led in, handed on to the platform, and seated on a throne forenenst the wonderful Feargal.

Feargal, with a curl on his lip, was viewing the champion who was to oppose him. The disdainful look that Johnny-One-Eye gave him in return delighted the hall-full, and rejoiced the heart of the King.

When everything was ready, the King sounded a bell, which was the signal for the champions to begin the greatest contest of learning Ireland ever knew, or ever would know.

Feargal the Scholar opened the ball—he held up a finger towards his opponent. That minute Johnny put up two fingers towards him. On the heels of that Feargal hoisted three fingers. Then the King's champion presented a closed fist. Feargal next put up a ripe strawberry, and Johnny-One-Eye put up a green gooseberry. The people, terribly anxious, quickly judged that, whatever it meant, things were going hard against Johnny, for he was getting red in the face with rage.

Feargal in a jiffy had up an apple that he took from his pocket. Then Johnny showed half a loaf of bread that he drew from under his coat. The gathering, to their sorrow, saw him, now, near foaming at the mouth, while Feargal was as cool as a trout in a pool.

Feargal next put the apple to his mouth and took a bite out of it; and the minute he did so, Johnny ups with the loaf, let it fly at Feargal's head, and laid him out like a corpse!

The King's scholars all jumped up together to demand that Johnny-One-Eye be hanged, drawn, and quartered; but, before they had time to sputter out of them the first words, Feargal was on his feet again, and crossing the platform, took Johnny's hand in both of his, and shook it as if he'd have it from the socket!

Turning then to the King and the dumfounded people, he proclaimed, "Your Royal Highness, and gentlemen, I frankly, freely, and publicly, to my shame, confess that, for the first time in his long career, Feargal the Scholar has been outmatched and disgraced—and here and now, I publicly withdraw all claims to scholarship."

"I've traveled far," went on Feargal, "gone to the world's most famous colleges, and contended with the world's most ingenious scholars, but I had to come among the High King's scholars at Tara," says he, "to meet this most supremely notable and extraordinary scholar, who, because his great learning exceeds all that I ever thought was in the power and mind of mortal man, has overthrown me. I am not only beaten, but actually proud of the distinction of being beaten by such an inconceivably great and immortal genius."

Says the King, getting to his feet, "Would you kindly expound to these assembled gentlemen all that passed between you and my champion?"

"I'll do that," says Feargal. "I first put up one finger, signifying that there was one God, which this profoundly learned gentleman well answered by putting up two fingers—meaning to say the Father had two other Persons along with Him. Then, thinking I had him caught, I exhibited three fingers, which meant, 'Then there are three Gods?' But your great Doctor, arising to the occasion, immediately closed his fist, indicating that they all, together, made one, Mighty and Indivisible.

"I held up a red strawberry to indicate that life is sweet; and the learned Doctor answered, with a green gooseberry, that life wasn't by any means all sweet, but was improved by having a judicious blending of the sour implicated in it.

"Next, myself exposed an apple to exemplify that, according to Holy Writ, fruit was the first and natural food of mankind; but the invincible dignitary instantly corrected me by exhibiting a loaf, asserting that bread was the staff of life, and that man was ordained to eat it in the sweat of his brow.

"Calling up all my brain power then, all my learning and inspiration, I took a bite out of my apple which meant to say, 'I have you at last; expound that if ye dare.' And lo, and behold ye! this most honorable and extraordinary genius, without giving me time to wink an eye, hurled his loaf at my head and laid me flat—in exemplification, as all of ye have perceived, that 'twas the biting of the apple that caused the Fall of Man.

"I'm finished!" says Feargal. "My disgrace is everlasting and complete. I only ask to be allowed to depart in peace, and be for evermore forgotten."

And sadly and sorrowfully, their heads between their legs, Feargal the Scholar and all his retinue—the greatest scholars of Kerry—departed from the King's palace—and from history.

Round Johnny-One-Eye (who had been listening, with mouth agape, to Feargal's speech) all the King's scholars and great doctors gathered, hoisting him on their shoulders, and nine times circumnavigating with him the King's castle. Then they bore him back to the hall, made the King hang him with all the medals, degrees, and learned orders of the kingdom, till the poor fellow's back bent to the breaking point.

"And now," says the King, says he, getting up from his throne, "there's one man we're forgetting, and 'twould ill become us not to remember and honor him. I call upon Dark Patrick," says he, "from Donegal, wherever he is, to come forth."

In a far-back corner of the room, under the choir loft, a little dark-whiskered man stood up and made his obedience to the King.

"Dark Patrick," says the King to the little black man from Donegal, "I have a fancy that I'd like to keep you about my court, and give you any salary you name, for doing nothing only just being handy any time I take the notion to seek your advice. Name your salary—and, no matter what it is, it'll be yours."

"Me lord," says Dark Patrick, "I humbly thank you with all my heart for your gracious goodness to one so unworthy. But you'll pardon me if, before replying to your demand, I request an Irishman's privilege of asking a question?"

"Certainly," says the King.

And says Dark Patrick, turning towards the seat where Johnny-One-Eye, all bewilderment, was stooping under his medals, "It is of the learned doctor on the platform," indicating Johnny, "that I'd ask the question."

"Feargal the Scholar," he went on, "kindly entertained this assembly with his point of view of the deaf-and-dumb discussion that passed between ye, and by means of which you, with your genius, floored the first scholar in the world. Now would you kindly honor this assembly with *your* account of the transaction?"

"Faith," says Johnny—"I'll do that same!—For 'twas mighty straight and simple. The lad ye put up against me," says he, "was the most ill-bred vagabond I ever had the bad fortune to cross in all my travels. He started by a remark on my personal peculiarities— holding up one finger to taunt me that I'd only one eye. As mad as a March hare, I put up two fingers to show that my one eye was as good as his two. Then carrying his taunts farther, he got up three fingers to draw an ill-natured laugh out of ye, expressing that here were two men with only three eyes in their company. I displayed my shut fist, to let him know what was waiting for him if he didn't quick change his tune. He ups with a strawberry to tell me he didn't care *that* for me. I ups with a green gooseberry to let him know back again I didn't care *that* for him, or for all his breed, seed, and generation. When the mean fellow then ups with an apple, taunting me that I was an apple-huckster's son, myself pulls out tuppence worth of bread that I was bringing home for my dinner when ye caught me and hauled me in here—I ups with the bread to let him know if he didn't soon halt his provocating and mend his manners, I'd brain him. But the impudent fellow, bent on his own ruination, immediately put the apple to his mouth and took a bite to remind me that when I was a youngster I used often to steal my poor old crippled mother's apples, run away, and eat them. That was the last straw —I let him have the loaf between the two eyes and stiffened him. 'Twas a great victory, so it was," says the innocent poor fellow.

"A great victory, entirely, it certainly was," says Dark Patrick. "And," says he, to Johnny, "I congratulate yourself, most learned sir, and all the other learned scholars here, on this most wonderful triumph."

"A terrible triumph, it surely was!" says the King, says he, taking a pinch of snuff. "And," says he, "I command that you, learned gentlemen, lead your new High Chief Doctor to the grandest suite of rooms your end of the castle knows, and attend on him with all reverence and honor henceforward. And now, as to yourself, Dark Patrick?" says the King, says he.

"Just, my Lord," says Dark Patrick, "what I was coming to. For your most generous offer to myself, my Lord," says he, "I regret I must reluctantly decline it. The likes of me, an ignorant poor mountain man, would be woefully out o' place in a Court that is inhabited by such great learned gentlemen as these I have the honor and the timorousness to see around me. Learning," says he, "is a wonderful thing, entirely. I heartily and humbly thank ye, my Lord," says he, making his obedience to the King, "and good-bye! 'Tis time I was shortening the road to my little cabin in the bogs of Donegal."

The King himself strove hard to hold him. But 'twas no use. Patrick hoisted on his stick the little bundle he traveled with, and them that looked after, soon saw him stepping out, lonely, but stoutly, on the road to the North.

THE WIDOW'S DAUGHTER

THERE was once a poor widow woman, living in Donegal, with a daughter Nabla, who grew up both idle and lazy, till, when she became a young woman, she was both thriftless and useless, only fit to sit with her heels in the ashes and croon to the cat the day long. One time, at length, her mother got so vexed for her refusing to do some little trifle about the house that she got a stick and began thrashing her.

Who should happen to ride by just then but the King's son; and when he heard the walloping and scolding, and crying and pleading within, he drew rein and shouted to know what was the matter. The widow came to the door, curtseying when she saw who he was, and, not wishing to put out a bad name on the girl, said that as she had a daughter who killed herself working, and refused to rest when her mother commanded, she had to be beaten into moderating her labor.

"That's surely a strange failing," says the King's son. "What work does your daughter do?"

"Spin, weave, sew, and everything that woman ever did," the mother replied.

Now, it so happened that a twelvemonth before the Prince had taken a notion to marry, and his mother, anxious that he should wed none but the best, had sent messengers around Ireland to find a woman who could perform all a woman's duties and especially the very three accomplishments the widow named; but all candidates who offered were unsatisfactory when put to the test, and the Prince had remained unwedded. So the Prince rejoiced when he heard the widow's charge against Nabla.

"You aren't fit to be mother or have charge of such a remarkable girl," said he. "For twelve months my mother has been searching out such a maid to make her my wife. I'll take Nabla with me."

Nabla was enchanted at this and her mother astonished. The King's son helped Nabla to a seat behind him and, bidding adieu to the widow, rode off.

To his mother, the Queen, he introduced Nabla, telling how by good fortune he had found the very woman they had so long looked for in vain. This wonderful girl could spin, weave and sew, and do everything else a woman should, and moreover was so eager for work that her mother was flailing her within an inch of her life to make her stop working when he arrived on the scene. The Queen said that was well. But she'd put her to the test anyway.

She took Nabla to a room where was a heap of raw silk and a silver wheel, and told her to have all the silk spun into thread before night—then left, locking the door after.

Poor Nabla, dumfounded, sat staring at the big heap of silk and the silver wheel till at length she began to cry. For she had never spun a yard of thread in all her life long.

Very soon an ugly old woman, with one of her feet as big as a bolster, appeared. "For what are you crying?" she asked Nabla.

She told her to have all the silk spun into thread before night—then left, locking the door after.

Nabla told her, and the old hag said, "I'll spin the silk for you if you promise to bid me to the wedding."

"I do that with heart and a half," Nabla said. And the old woman sat to the wheel, and, working it with the big foot, spun the heap in less than no time.

When the Queen came and found all spun she said, "That is good." Next day she gave Nabla a golden loom and told Nabla she must have all the thread woven in webs before night. And locking the door, she left Nabla looking, distracted, from the thread to the loom, and from the loom to the thread—for she hadn't, in her life, once thrown a shuttle. At length she laid her face in her hands and began to cry.

Soon there appeared an ugly old woman with one hand big as a pot hanging by her side. She asked Nabla why she cried, and Nabla told her. Then the hag said,

"I'll do the weaving for you if you'll promise to bid me to your wedding."

"I'll surely do that, and welcome," Nabla said.

So the old one sat to the loom and, throwing the shuttle with her great big hand, very soon had all the thread woven in webs.

When the Queen came and found the work done she said, "That is good."

Next day she gave Nabla a gold needle and thimble, and said that before night, she must have all the webs made in shirts for the Prince and his friends.

When the Queen had gone, Nabla, who had never even threaded a needle in her life, sat, wildly looking from the needle and thimble to the webs of silk. And again she broke down and began crying her eyes out.

An ugly old hag with monstrous big nose that weighed her head down appeared and asked why she cried.

Nabla told her, and the ugly old one said, "I'll make the webs into shirts for the Prince if you'll bid me to your wedding."

"I'll do that," Nabla said, "and a thousand welcomes."

So the old woman, taking the needle and thimble, sat down, and, with her big nose drooping into her work, in short time had all the webs wrought into shirts and disappeared again.

When the Queen came and found all the silk made in shirts, she was mightily pleased and said, "You are the woman for my son. He'll never need to call in a spinner, a weaver, or a seamstress while you live."

Then Nabla and the Prince were betrothed, and on the wedding day there was a gay and gorgeous company in the Palace hall. All was mirth and festivity, and everyone past himself or herself with happiness and delight.

Everyone, that is excepting the one who should be happiest of all, Nabla. Instead of being happy her heart was weighted with despair, for thinking of what would happen to her the first time her husband asked her to spin or to weave or to make him a shirt.

As the company seated themselves to the long tables to begin the wedding feast, there came a loud knock on the door at the bottom of the hall, and when a servant opened it, the Prince and all his guests were astonished to behold enter an ugly old hag who, lifting and laying one great big foot, came hirpledy-hop, hirpledy-hop, all the way up the floor to where the Prince sat at the head table with his bride!

When the ugly old hag reached there, the Prince politely arose and bowed to her saying, "You're welcome, madam, to my wedding. May I ask whose bidding are you?"

And the old hag answered, "I'm the bride's bidding."

"Then you're double welcome," said the Prince, believing she was one of Nabla's poor friends. He ordered room to be made for her by the bride's right hand, and as she sat down, he asked, "Would you mind, dear madam, telling the company and myself what made your foot so big?" And she answered, "I've been a lifetime working the spinning wheel with it, till all the blood in my body ran into the foot, leaving me the spectacle you are beholding."

"Then by my word," said the Prince, striking the table a great blow, "my beautiful bride shall never put foot to a wheel while I'm alive to prevent it!" And he ordered the feast to begin.

But as the party would settle to their feasting, a great knock sounded on the door, everyone turned to look, and when a servant opened it, in walked a woman with one hand as big as a stool. The weight of the hand hanging by her side gave her body a monstrous lean-over, so that as she hobbled up the floor, the company at the tables, watching, were silent in surprise.

When she reached him, the Prince politely arose and bowed to her, saying, "You are welcome to my wedding, madam. May I ask whose bidding are you?"

And the hag answered, "I'm the bride's bidding."

"Then you're double welcome," said the Prince, believing she, too, was one of Nabla's poor friends. He ordered room to be made for her. And as she sat down, he asked, "Would you mind, dear madam, telling the company and myself what made your hand so big?"

"Weaving," she answered him. "I have slaved at the loom, throwing the shuttle all my life, till all the blood in my body ran into the hand, leaving it the spectacle as you see."

"Then," said the Prince, striking the table a thundering blow, "by my word, my wife shall never throw a shuttle again while I live to prevent it. On with the feast," he said.

But, as the company would begin, a great knock on the door startled them. Every one turned, and saw the servant admit an ugly old woman with the greatest nose ever beheld or dreamt of! Up the floor she waddled, her weighed head wagging from side to side—up the floor, and up the floor.

When she reached the head table, the Prince politely arose and bowed to her, saying, "Madam, you're welcome to my wedding. But may I ask whose bidding are you?"

And she answered, "I'm the bride's bidding."

"Then you're thrice welcome," said the Prince, believing she also was one of Nabla's poor friends. He ordered room to be made for her, and as she sat down, he asked, "Would you mind, dear madam, telling the company and myself what made your nose so big?"

"It's from sewing," she said. "All my life I've been stooping my head over shirts a-sewing, till every drop of blood in my body ran down into my nose, making it the monster you're beholding."

The Prince struck the table a blow that made all the dishes

bounce. "By my word," he said, "my wife shall never thread a needle again, or do any other sort of housework while I live to prevent it!"

Nabla's low heart now leapt to hit the roof. At once she was the happiest of the hundreds of happy ones there, and the day that had begun dark and despairful for her turned the very brightest, very joyfullest, of all her life.

The Prince faithfully kept his word. He was always on watch to catch Nabla spinning, weaving, sewing, or doing any kind of work that woman ever did. He even hired spies to report to him if she tried to work in secret.

Nabla, however, never did anything to make him uneasy, but, forgiving her old mother and taking her to live in the castle with her, she ever after lived happy and content and lazy as the day was long.

DONAL O'DONNELL'S

STANDING ARMY

A MAN by the name of Donal O'Donnell, with his wife Sally, lived in a little house on a hillside in Donegal. He'd been married on Sally a lachy while, but hadn't any children and was getting on in years. Hard times came down upon them, and poverty slouched in at the door. It went from hard to harder until, at long last, when they got up one morning they hadn't a pick to put in their mouth. Sally, who was never the sweetest-tempered woman in the world, but had a tongue and a temper that were small comfort to any man, now tongue-banged Donal beyond the beyonds, put him out, and commanded him to be off with him and not show his face again till he had got something to put them out of their poverty.

Donal said little, but spat on his stick and traveled afore him for the length of a lee-long summer day.

In the evening he threw himself on a green knowe (knoll), feeling down-hearted entirely. Not long was he stretched there when he heard music from somewhere. And soon he discovered a round hollow hollowed out of the knowe's top. And behold, when he gleeked over, there in the bottom of this hollow were scores upon scores of Little People singing, dancing, and feasting. There were tables and tables outspread with white tablecloths, carrying the most enticing eatables and drinkables that Donal had ever beheld in all his born life. 'Twas a sight that made his mouth water. He craned his neck over the edge, and put three roars out of him that created consternation below. The Little People suspended their dancing, their feasting, and fun-making, and huddled together with the fright. But one of them, bolder, a little lad with green jacket, came climbing up to Donal. "Donal, Donal," says he, "what's wrong with you, or what is it that you want?"

"By this and by that," says Donal, says he, "I'll go down and not leave two of you alive, nor two pieces of one of you together, unless you send me up something to put myself and Sally out of our poverty."

"If you'll only have mercy," says the little man, "we'll soon do that."

Back he went, and 'twas short time till he was up again and with him a wee Blue Duck, which he gave to Donal, saying, "Neither yourself nor Sally need ever be in poverty any more, for every time you set this duck on a nest and say to it, 'Blue Duck, Blue Duck, do your duty,' it will lay you a golden egg."

"Let me see," says Donal. He set down the Blue Duck and said, "Blue Duck, Blue Duck, do your duty," and lo and behold, the Blue Duck laid him a golden egg!

Right hearty Donal thanked the little fellow, and putting the Duck under his coat, spat on his staff, and started for home, a hearty, happy man.

But night came down on him ere he had gone far, and meeting a house, he said to himself that he'd put up there for the night; so in he stepped, asking for supper and a shake-down.

They gave him his supper, and a shake-down. But before he bedded Donal gave them the Blue Duck for safe-keeping, saying as he did so, "Take prime care of this little animal for me, but on your life's peril, don't put it on a nest and say to it, 'Blue Duck, Blue Duck, do your duty.' "

"Oh, no, no," says they. "For why should we?"

No sooner, though, was Donal in bed and asleep than the man and woman, sitting, chatting, over the fire, began wondering why Donal had laid such injunction on them. And said the woman, "Just for the fun of it, let us try till we see what'll happen." Down they set the Blue Duck on a nest and said to it, "Blue Duck, Blue Duck, do your duty"—and instantly the Duck laid them a golden egg!

"By this and by that," says they, " 'tis the most precious thing we ever knew or heard tell of. 'Twould be mortal pity to let that duck go, for we'd never be poor again while we have it."

No sooner said than done. They changed the duck for one of their own that looked just like it; and in the morning, Donal went off happy with their blue duck under his arm, instead of the real one.

When Donal reached home, he wasn't in at the door till he cried to Sally, "Sally, dear, we're never going to be poor any more."

"I'm glad of it," says Sally. "Insense me why."

"Because," says Donal, "here's a wee Blue Duck I have with me, and all we need do when we want money, is put it on a nest and say to it, 'Blue Duck, Blue Duck, do your duty,' and it will lay a golden egg!"

"Well, well," says Sally, "that's the miraclessest thing I ever heard tell of. Try it till we see."

"I'll not try it," says Donal, "till you gather in the neighbors, that we may astound them and water their mouths for our great fortune."

In rapid time Sally spread the alarm and the neighbors were trooping in, and crowding the house from hearthstone to threshold.

When they were all in, Donal said, "Now keep your mouths shut and your eyes open, boys and girls, till you see what you'll see!"

He made a nice wee nest upon the table, on it set the Duck,

and said to it, "Blue Duck, Blue Duck, do your duty!" But lo, never a thing did the Duck do but close one eye and quack!

Says Donal, "It must be I didn't speak loud enough." And he said, louder, "Blue Duck! Blue Duck! Do your duty!"

But never an egg, gold, silver, wood, or brass, appeared! Poor Donal was in a quandary. Says he, "It's deaf that duck has got since last night. But he's going to hear me this time, or I'll know why."

And this time he shouted to dinnle the roof's rafters, "Blue Duck! Blue Duck! I'm telling you, do your duty!" But instead of laying a golden egg, the duck was so frightened that it rose up and flew around the house, screeching, and swiping the neighbors' eyes out.

Red mad, the congregation began bawling that Donal had made idiot fools of them. And they fell on him and gave him a great drubbing entirely.

But if the neighbors were severe on him, Sally was ten times more so. With a besom she banged him out of the house again, and told him begone and not to dare show his face again till he'd surely have something to put them out of their poverty.

Away and away before him Donal traveled, for the length of a night and the lee-long day. In the heel o' the evening he reached again the self-same green knowe and threw himself down on it, weary and worn. Behold, he wasn't lying long till he heard fierce singing and music. Up he starts and gleeks down into the bowl on top and there sees hundreds and hundreds of the Little People, singing, dancing, feasting, and merry-making. Donal let out of him three such odious roars as threw them below into marvelous consternation. Up comes the little lad in the green jacket again, and, "Donal, Donal," says he, "what's the matter anyhow, or what is it you want now?"

"A purty way you handled me," says Donal—and he up and told how the duck refused to lay at all when he got home and had the neighbors gathered to admire the performance. "And by this end and by that," says he, "I have come now to massacray all of you. I'll not leave one of you alive, nor two pieces of any one together!"

"Oh!" says the little lad. "What would you take, and show mercy to us?"

"Well," says Donal, "if you or any one of you want to live any longer you had better give me, quick, something that will put Sally and myself out of our poverty."

Down again went the little fellow, and not long till he came back with a napkin. Says he, "Here's a napkin, and whenever you out-spread it and say to it: 'Napkin! Napkin! serve all sorts,' it will be a tablecloth covered with the rarest of eatables and drinkables—enough to feed a regiment. As long as you possess it," says he, "yourself and Sally will never know poverty more."

"Let me try it," says Donal, "and see. I'm purty hungry this minute anyhow."

Down on the grass he laid the napkin, and said to it, "Napkin! Napkin! serve all sorts." And such a feast as was instantly before him, he'd never beheld in all his life before. A right hearty meal he made, and then, rolling up the napkin, put it in his pocket, and away with him, rejoicing.

The darkness was down on him as he met up with the same wee house on the roadside; so he entered and asked for supper and a bed.

They welcomed Donal, and said he would have both, with heart-and-a-half. And when Donal had eaten his supper, they showed him to a bed in the room above. But he first gave the woman charge of his napkin, saying, "This little napkin I'm very particular about, and I want you to keep it safe for me till morning. Be careful with it," says he, "but above all things, and on your life's peril, don't open it up, and say to it: 'Napkin! Napkin! serve all sorts.' "

The woman said "Surely not. For why should we do that?"

When they had Donal in bed and asleep, and themselves sitting, chatting, over the fire, says the woman, says she, "I wonder why it is that he doesn't want us to spread out that napkin and say to it, 'Napkin! Napkin! serve all sorts?'—for the fun of the thing, let us just try."

On the table she spread the napkin and said to it, "Napkin! Napkin! serve all sorts," and instantly was served such a feast of eatables and drinkables, the rarest that man or mortal ever dreamt of. And down they sat and ate a great meal, entirely.

Then they said it would be a mortal pity to let such a grand thing go with Donal; so they changed it for another napkin of the selfsame appearance, and gave the mock one to Donal departing in the morning.

When he reached home Sally hailed him. "I hope you had better luck this time and brought us something to put us out of our poverty."

"Oh, Sally, Sally dear," says Donal. "We'll never in our lives know want or poverty more."

"How is that?" says Sally.

"Because," says he, "here's a little napkin, and whenever we're hungry or thirsty, all we have to do is spread it on the table and say to it, 'Napkin! Napkin! serve all sorts,' and there will instantly be out-spread a gorgeous feast for a hundred men."

"Well, well," says Sally, says she, "that's extraordinary entirely. Spread it there till we see."

"Oh, no, no," says Donal, says he. "I want to have the crow over the neighbors this time. I'll not spread it till you gather them in. Then we'll provoke them with a feast that will leave them licking their lips for a month of Sundays."

Well and good. Off went Sally with the great news of what Donal had brought back with him, and the neighbors came flocking to Donal's, filling the house from hearthstone to threshold.

"Now," says Donal, says he, when they were all there, "keep your senses sharp and your eyes open, for the performance is about to begin."

On the table he spread the napkin and says to it, "Napkin! Napkin! serve all sorts."

But the sorra a crumb appeared upon the napkin. Donal shouted at it, roared, bawled, yelled, and screeched—but if he was to screech till he tore the roof off, sorra a particle, eatable, or drinkable would appear!

"Well, well, well!" says Donal, desperate, "that beats the wee wheel that ground the millstone—I protest to ye, one and all, I saw with my own two eyes that little napkin work a miracle!"

But the neighbors fell upon the poor fellow and gave him an unconscienceable drubbing out and out. But if they abused him, Sally ill-used him ten times worse, after, and a sore and sorry man was Donal.

The very next morning, off Sally turned him again, and warned him that if he didn't this time surely find something to put them out of their poverty, he darsen't put his nose in the door evermore.

With his heart down in his shoes, off Donal tramped, away and away for the length of a long summer's day—till evening came and he was weary and ready to drop.

Reaching the same green knowe once more, Donal threw himself on it. But not long was he lying till he heard great singing and music. Looking down the hollow in the knowe's crown, he beheld crowds upon crowds of Little People singing and dancing, feasting and carousing. Donal put three great roars out of him that immediately threw the whole party into paralysed consternation.

The little man in the green jacket came tearing up to Donal immediately, and says he, "Donal, Donal, what's the matter, or what's a-trouble to you anyway?"

Says Donal, "I'll have the life of every soul of ye, and I'll not leave two pieces of one of you together for the pitiful way you have handled me," commencing and telling how the napkin was of no more use to him than the duck.

So the little fellow, says he, "Donal, did you stop or stay anywhere from you left here till you got home?"

"I stopped nowhere," says Donal, says he, "only in a decent house by the roadside, where I got clean and kind lodging for the night."

"Ah, hah!" says the little fellow, says he, "Just hold on there a minute till I see what can be done."

Down he descended again, and after a while came up with a wee caubeen (little rimless hat).

"Here," says he, "Donal, is something that will rightify you and get you out of all difficulties, now and evermore. Any time you lay this caubeen on the ground and say to it: 'Caubeen! Caubeen! display your ability' there will jump out of it ten Wee Men with blackthorns, squaring their sticks overhead and asking to see the enemy. Nothing on two feet will be able to withstand them. They'll ludher and lambaste your enemies to the height and depth of satisfaction—and till you care to call 'Retreat.' Stop tonight again at the wee house where they surely cheated you; perform the self-same round as before, and leave it to this caubeen to get you your true duck and napkin and send you home happy."

"That's very wonderful entirely," says Donal, "and I'll give it a try."

That night he reached the wee house by the roadside, went in, and with many a word of blarney to the pair who were there, asked for the privilege of a bite and a bed.

They welcomed Donal heartily, and said he would have both, with heart-and-a-half. Before he went off to his bed, he handed over the caubeen to the woman of the house, saying he wanted her to take particular care of it till morning. "But above all," says Donal, "I want ye to be very sure, and on your life's peril, not to say to it, 'Caubeen! Caubeen! display your ability!' "

"Indeed and 'deed we will not," says she. "For why should we do that?"

My brave Donal wasn't long in bed, and pretending to be fast asleep, when he was afoot again and listening at the room door. He overheard them producing the caubeen and admiring it, and the woman wondering why he didn't want them to lay it down and say to it, "Caubeen! Caubeen! display your ability." "For the fun of it, I'd just like to try," says she.

Laying the caubeen then on the floor, she says, "Caubeen! Caubeen! display your ability!" Instantly out of it sprang ten little men with blackthorns, squaring which overhead, they leapt at herself and her old man and began to ludher, and lay on, thrash and smash, wallop and whack them, up the floor, down the floor, and round the floor, making them hop, skip, and jump, roar, scream, screech, and yell, calling on Donal for Heaven and Hell's sake to come and call off his troops—or they'd be murdered by them, out and out!

But not till they'd got the walloping and ludhering they sore needed and deserved did Donal step on the scene, laughing heart-breakingly and enjoying the predicament their old roguery had introduced them to. To their praying and pleading, begging and beseeching, Donal, after they were trounced and thrashed to his pleasement, bid the rogues produce the napkin and the duck they had deprived him of. In double-quick time they consented, and Donal only then called "Retreat," and the little men lowered their weapons and disappeared into the caubeen again. And with his three prizes, Donal set out for home, delighted and happy.

When Donal reached home Sally met him with, "I hope you have brought us something at last to put us out of our poverty."

Says Donal, "I have very wonderful things, entirely, for you this time, Sally, and we're going never to know want nor worry more."

"What is it you have?" says Sally.

"I'll not tell you that," says Donal, "till you gather in all the neighbors that they may enjoy our good fortune with us."

In quick time the countryside was flocking into Donal's, they smudging and nudging and sniggering among themselves, expecting the delight of delivering to Donal another drubbing.

When he had them all together, Donal laid down the Blue Duck on a nest, and, appropriately addressing it, had the delight of beholding the eyes of the neighbors swell the size of saucers with wonderment when, every time he commanded, the Duck laid a golden egg!

"Ye think that wonderful," says Donal, "but it's nothing to what I'm yet to show ye."

He spread his napkin on the table, and at his demand there was outspread the rarest and richest of eating and drinking for a hundred men! And the astounded onlookers, at Donal's invitation, fell to and made the greatest feast they had ever made in their lives before. And they exclaimed and wondered again and again at the wonderful luck of Donal. And Sally, she was dumfounded entirely.

When all had eaten and drunk their hearty fill, Donal said, "But I've the wonderfullest miracle of all to display to ye yet." Down on the ground he set the caubeen and says to it, "Caubeen! Caubeen! display your ability!" when out jumps the ten Wee Men brandishing blackthorns and starts laying on the multitude. The Wee Men walloped and whacked, licked and ludhered, thrashed, crashed, and smashed right, left, and center; the neighbors yelled, and screamed, and bawled, and screeched, hopped, leapt, bounded, and jumped round and round the house. Donal, he stood by, his hands in his pockets, roaring and laughing, and egging on his troops—the heart of him delighted to hear the leapers and hoppers imploring, begging, beseeching him to call off his men—Sally, the loudest and beseechingest of them all!

But off or off, Donal wouldn't call them, till they had given the gathering the soundest thrashing and malavoguing they had ever got in their lives, hardly leaving a whole bone in the body of one of them. When the little men had ludhered and lathered the neighbors out of the door and were ready to return to the caubeen again, Donal noticed Sally crouching in a corner, watching in consternation. And, "Now, Sally," says he, "your temper hasn't been as sweet as it might have been lately, and I think a little of the same medicine the neighbors got mightn't be one bit harmful, but wholesome, healthy, and beneficial for yourself." So he set the Little Men to operate upon Sally and give her the drubbing she sore needed—and it was only after she'd got the father and mother of a sound bleaching that then he called off his troops and sent them into their caubeen again.

Then, "Sally," says he, "I think that little lesson will do you a world of good for the remainder of your days." And it did so.

With the produce of his Duck, Donal built a castle with a window for every day in the year.

By virtue of his napkin, he gave to the nobility of the country dinners, feasts, and banquets that were never equaled in Ireland before or since. Open house he kept for the world's population. And no poor man coming to his door ever left his door poor again.

Sally turned into an obedient, kindly, sweet-tempered woman, and a parable for the country. For the remainder of their days, she and Donal lived content, happy, and snug as hares in harvest —and gave thanks to the good God every morning they rose up and every night they lay down.

Donal proclaimed himself King, with a standing army living in a caubeen and costing him nothing—such an army as the kings of the world would trade their crowns for—but in vain.

And never, from that long-ago day to this, has perished or even paled the fame and name of the great Donal O'Donnell and his Standing Army.

THE WELL

O' THE WORLD'S END

ONCE upon a time, and a good time it was, there were a King and
Queen in Ireland who had one son, Conor, a brave boy whom
both King and Queen loved very much. But the Queen died
when he was a child, and the King married again. The new
Queen had three sons whom she worshipped—though they were
far from being as fine boys as was Conor. And she disliked Conor
just as much as she loved her own sons. Most she disliked him
because, as the King loved him dearly, he would inherit the kingdom instead of one of her own boys.

When the boys grew to be young men, and Conor showed
himself every day finer and braver and more and more beloved
of the world, she made up her mind to get rid of him, by hook
or by crook. She consulted a hen-wife, who lived in a wee hut
close to the castle; and the hen-wife told her that the one way to
get rid of Conor was to take to her bed and pretend she was
dying, and have her doctor say that the only thing that could
cure her was three bottles of water from the Well o' the World's

End—and she should then call on Conor to fetch her the cure, which, as was known, no man could do and come back alive.

The Queen said this was good. She took to her bed and pretended to be dying, and her doctor proclaimed that the only thing that could cure her was three bottles of water from the Well o' the World's End.

She then called Conor and put *geasa* on him to go to the Well o' the World's End and bring back from there three bottles of water for her curing. As *geasa* was an honor obligation that no man could shirk, poor Conor had to accept—though he felt that it surely meant his death. He was sad, and his father was sadder still.

As he was, in turn, privileged to put *geasa* on her, Conor said, "I request that you order your three sons to accompany me, and that yourself, who are not sick, but pretending, watch from the top of the tallest tower of my father's castle, and never leave your post till you see the four of us returning—your food to be what grains blown from the corn-fields you grab from the winds, and your drink what rain-drops you catch in your mouth."

The Queen was enraged when she heard her sentence—but had to accept it. Conor got his broken-hearted father's blessing and, taking the Queen's three sons with him, set out. Looking back from the first hilltop as he rode away, he saw the evil woman begin her weary watch from the tower.

Away and away they rode, by hills and howes [hillocks] and thorny knowes [knolls], by green valley, moor, and mountain, by waving woods, shimmering lochs, and singing streams, by fairy raths and the Great Green Plain of Dreams—away and away, far farther than I could tell you, twice farther than you could tell me, and ten times farther than anyone else could tell the two of us—till, at length and at last, one evening late, they came in sight of a wonderful house built of scarlet logs, on a faraway hilltop. To it they pushed and, going in, beheld crouching over the fire an old, old man with a great long white beard. He looked round and said, "You are welcome, Conor, the King of Ireland's son, and your three half-brothers with you. Come tell me why you have come so very, very far, and are leaving the world behind you."

"It isn't with willing heart I'm leaving the world behind me," said Conor. "But the Queen of Ireland is sick and says she cannot be cured till she gets three bottles of water from the Well o' the World's End, and has laid *geasa* on me to fetch it."

"I'm sorry for you, Conor," said the old man. "Three hundred years have I lived here, and a thousand of the world's renowned champions I have seen come this way, faring for the Well o' the World's End—but when they learned of the dread perils and dangers that lay before them, seven hundred turned back, and of the three hundred who went forward, no one of them ever returned alive."

When he heard that, the youngest of the three brothers instantly turned to stone with fright.

The old man asked the remaining three to have supper with him and sleep there that night, and he would see what he could do to help them in the morning. He cut down a rabbit that was seasoning in the chimney, roasted it, and on it all made a hearty supper and left the full of a basket of leavings.

Very well and good. They slept soundly, and when they had had breakfast off the rabbit's leavings in the morning, the old man said, "I have a brother three hundred years older than me, who lives a thousand miles from here, and he may be able to help you. Here's a copper ball I'll throw before you: fast as it goes, you will follow as fast, and reach his house tonight."

He hurled the bounding ball ahead of them and after it they followed. No bird ever flew as fast as the ball bounded. But fast as the ball went, they found their feet going every bit as fast—away and away, by hills and howes and thorny knowes, by green valley, moor, and mountain, by waving woods, shimmering lochs, and singing streams, by fairy raths and the Great Green Plain of Dreams—away and away, far farther than I could tell you, twice farther than you could tell me, and ten times farther than anyone else could tell the two of us—till, late that evening, they beheld a strange house of sky-blue logs on a hillside.

To this house they pushed. And when they entered, saw, crouched over the fire, an old, old, very old man whose white beard touched his knees. He looked round and said, "You are welcome, Conor, the King of Ireland's son, and your two half-brothers with you. Come, sit at the fire and tell me why it is that you have come so dreadful far, and are leaving the world behind you."

Said Conor, "It isn't with willing heart I'm leaving the world behind me, but the Queen of Ireland is sick, and says she cannot be cured till she gets three bottles of water from the Well o' the World's End, and she has laid *geasa* on me to fetch it."

"I am sorry indeed for you," said the old man. "Six hundred years I have lived, and in that time saw three hundred of the world's most renowned champions reach here, faring for the Well o' the World's End, but when they learned of the dreadful perils and dangers that lay before them, two hundred turned back, and of those who went forward, no one of them ever returned alive."

When the second of Conor's half-brothers heard that, he was instantly turned to stone with fright.

"However," said the old man, "sit down and have supper and rest for the night, and I'll see what I can do to help you in the morning."

From the chimney where he had it seasoning, the old man took down half a rabbit, roasted it on the coals; and on it they made a hearty supper and left three baskets of leavings.

They slept soundly, and in the morning, after they had breakfasted on the rabbit's leavings, the old man said, "I have a brother three hundred years older than me, who lives three thousand miles from here, who may be able to aid you. I'll give you, to guide you there, a swallow, the swiftest in the world. But swift as the bird is, everyone who follows is just as swift." And he launched forth the magic bird.

They thanked him and set out. The swallow flew a hundred times faster than the swiftest they had ever seen; but swift as flew the swallow, their feet went every bit as swift. They followed by hills and howes and thorny knowes, by green valley, moor, and mountain, by waving woods, shimmering lochs, and singing streams, by fairy raths and the Great Green Plain of Dreams—away and away, far farther than I could tell you, twice farther than you could tell me, and ten times farther than anyone else could tell the two of us. And late that evening they saw on a distant hilltop a house of shining, white logs—which they drew upon.

They entered, and there beheld crouched over the fire an old, old, very, very old man, whose beard swept the floor. And this very old man turned and said, "You are welcome, Conor, the King of Ireland's son, and your half-brother with you. Come, sit down and tell me why it is you have come so far and dreadful far, and are leaving the world behind you."

"It isn't with willing heart I'm leaving the world behind me," said Conor, "but the Queen of Ireland is sick, and says she cannot be cured till she gets three bottles of water from the Well o' the World's End, and she has laid *geasa* on me to fetch it."

"I'm sorry, and very, very sorry for you," said the old, old man. "I have lived here nine hundred years, and during that time, saw a hundred of the world's champions reach here, faring for the Well o' the World's End, but when they learned of the dread perils and dangers that lay before them, ninety-nine turned back and the only one who went forward never returned again."

When Conor's half-brother heard that, he instantly turned to stone with fright.

"But sit down and have supper," said the old man, "and sleep here tonight, and in the morning I'll see what I can do to help you."

Out of the chimney, where he had it seasoning, the very old man took down a quarter of rabbit and roasted it on the coals, and after the two of them had made hearty supper on it, they had seven baskets of leavings.

Right well Conor slept. And in the morning, after he and the old man had breakfasted on the rabbit's leavings, the old man said, "Conor, you have come, as you know, on the most perilous adventure ever known since time began. The Well o' the World's End lies in the lawn of the Queen of the Hill of the

World's End on an island ten thousand miles from here. Her Castle is surrounded by a wall nine miles high, a mile wide, and a hundred miles around. That wall has on it three hundred and sixty-five corners, and on every corner is a tower, and in every tower are a hundred guards with flaming swords, and traversing the wall-top are ten thousand tigers, leopards, and roaring lions, so that if any champion could ever scale the wall, he never could reach the Well alive."

"That's sad, and bad, and very bad," said Conor, as his heart sank.

"Sad and bad it is," said the old man. "But," said he, "once in every seven hundred years, on every man, woman, beast, and bird—on every living creature in and around the Castle of the Hill o' the World's End falls magic sleep for an hour. As it luckily happens, it is now very near seven hundred years since the Sleep Hour was with them—in a few days' time it is due again, at noon. It is your one and only chance if you can reach the castle in time for the Sleep Hour. We'll have to make greatest haste."

He led Conor with him down to the seashore, and plucking a May-flower from the bank, threw it on the waters, where it instantly arose up a full-rigged ship with crew complete. "That ship," said the old man, "will take you swiftly to the Island o' the World's End. When you reach there, you have still far and far to go till you come to the Castle of the Queen of the Hill o' the World's End. Here's a bridle," said he, giving to Conor a silver bridle with golden bit and reins of silk. "When you reach Land of the World's End, step ashore and shake the bridle three times. Bounding to you will come a handsome brown colt. But you are to say to it, 'No, no!' It will then trot away. Again shake the bridle three times, and a beautiful black filly will come prancing to you. You are to say to it, 'No, no!'—and the filly will trot off again. Shake the bridle once again three times, and to you will come staggering an old grey nag, with bones showing through the skin, and rattling as it runs. Bridle and mount him and he will take you safely and swiftly to the Hill. If you are fortunate enough to be in time for the Sleep Hour, the old grey horse will see you over the wall. Do not stop or stay till you have got your bottles of water from the Well on the castle lawn;

and then, no matter how enchanting or tempting the sounds you hear or the scenes you see, on the peril of your life don't stop, stay, dally, pause, or delay, but mount with all speed, put the nag to the wall again, and make your escape."

Conor promised to follow directions faithfully, thanked the old man, and stepped aboard the ship. Instantly, the white sails flapped, the tall masts strained, the timbers creaked, and the ship started off, skimming the water with the speed of a sunbeam. For seven days and seven nights it sped, till, on the eighth morning, it ran on the shore of a dazzling land, the Island o' the World's End.

Taking his bridle, Conor leaped on land. There he shook the bridle three times, and a handsome brown colt came bounding to him. Conor said, "No, no!" and the brown colt disappeared again. He shook the bridle again three times, and a beautiful black filly came prancing to him. To the filly Conor said, "No, no!" and it trotted off again. A third time he gave the bridle three shakes—and that instant there appeared, staggering toward him, the sorriest, most miserable old grey nag he had ever laid eyes on, the old bones of it making a noise like thunder. When the skinny beast came up, Conor bridled it with the silver bridle that had the golden bit and, mounting, headed inland.

The old grey steed shamed the lightning for speed. It overtook the wind before, and the wind behind couldn't overtake it. It was only touching with its toes the tops of the highest hills. The sparks from his heels were striking the moon behind, and the sparks from its toes hitting the sun in front. Like that it sped for a day and a night, and on the next day, nearing noon, Conor beheld, far off, on a great green hill, a shining, dazzling, blinding castle with thirteen domes; around it a wall, nine miles high, a mile wide, and a hundred miles around. The wall had three hundred and sixty-five corners, and on every corner was a tower, and in every tower were a hundred men armed with flaming swords, the glowing and glancing of which afar off were stabbing the eyes of Conor. But it was the frightening, thunderous roaring and screaming of ten thousand tigers, panthers, and lions, deafening the skies as they paraded the walls, that stopped Conor's heart's beating and paralyzed his senses complete. His heart sank like a lump of lead, and he cried out, "I am lost!"—when a miracle happened. The flaming swords and men who bore them dropped, the ear-splitting roars ceased, the lions, tigers, and leopards froze in their tracks, a dead silence came down on the whole world.

The Sleep Hour had descended on all!

Soon as Conor's shocked senses returned to him he spurred his old grey steed and headed for the castle wall, cleared it at a bound—and alighted on the most magnificent great green lawn the eye of man had ever beheld. He couldn't see its bounds on either side. The sights and sounds were ravishing, and the air was filled with rarest fragrance and sweetest music, coming from he didn't know where. But remembering his warning, he neither halted nor paused till he found in the lawn's center, the Well o' the World's End, where he filled three bottles with its water.

So entrancing to him was the shining castle which uprose before him that, saying to himself he had time to spare, he thought it would be no harm to take one quick look into the castle's grand hall. He hitched his horse to the golden railing in front of the grand entrance, and stepped into a hall paved with precious stones, its walls glittering with diamonds and pearls. From the hall he got glimpse of a grand dining room, which he thought it would be no harm, for one little moment, to step into. And then to seat himself, for just one second, in a jewelled chair at head of a beauteous table spread with a white linen cloth. Said Conor, who was feeling hungry, "I wish there was a good dinner on that cloth." And immediately there was on the cloth the greatest, grandest dinner that the heart of man could desire. For the cloth was a wishing cloth. Among the varieties on the table was a ham, the sweetest he had ever tasted—and such that the more he cut it, the bigger it grew. And a loaf of bread was there, the finest and whitest and most toothsome he had ever known—and such that the more he ate of it, the greater it got. And a jug of nectar was there, the most ravishing he had ever tasted—and such that the more he drank of it, the fuller it became.

When the skinny beast came up, Conor bridled it with the silver bridle that had the golden bit.

When Conor had eaten and drunk to his heart's content, he gathered with him the cloth, the ham, the loaf, and the bottle of nectar, and venturing into the next room—a magnificent drawing room—beheld a sight that spellbound him! On a silken couch lay asleep the loveliest maiden that had ever on his eyesight dawned —the Queen of the Hill of the World's End. And asleep on nine other silken couches were nine beautiful maids, her ladies-in-waiting. He couldn't move for many minutes, but stood entranced gazing on the Queen's beauty.

Suddenly it struck him that his hour must be almost up. He darted to the Queen's couch, kissed her, and snatching a ring off her finger, broke it, put one part in his pocket and tied the other part, with one of her silk ribbons, around her neck. Then, gathering with him, in the dining room, the magic ham, loaf and jug, he dashed from the castle, bounded on his steed's back, and sped for the walls.

When he reached it, his steed he quick put to the wall but, lo! to his terror the horse only went within a mile of the top and fell back! That moment the warriors in the towers and the wild beasts on the walls gave the first stir of their awaking, and every leaf on every tree on the lawn shivered.

Like the brave fellow he was, he wheeled the animal, put spurs to him, and went at the wall again. The horse just touched the wall's top with his toes and fell back! The warriors in the towers and the wild animals on the walls gave the second stir of their awakening. And every tree on the lawn quaked and every stone in the great walls groaned.

The brave fellow wheeled his horse again, put spurs to him, and set him at the wall a third time. At that instant every warrior in the towers, and every wild beast on the walls, gave the third and final stir of their awakening—clouds thundered, skies sundered, and the whole world quivered and wondered.

The old grey nag cleared the walls, the roaring beasts, and the raging warriors—and landed Conor safely on the other side!

Like lightning they sped, the grey horse overtaking the wind before, and the wind behind unable to overtake it. Its hooves lightly touched the tops of the highest hills. The sparks from its heels were striking the moon behind, and the sparks from its toes striking the sun in front. And in small time they reached the harbor where the ship was waiting. Conor jumped off, thanked the old nag, pulled off and shook the bridle, and the steed shook his head and sped off. Aboard his ship Conor bounded, the white sails flapped, the tall masts strained, the timbers creaked, and the ship was skimming the seas swifter than lightning; and never sail was slacked or ship tacked till they ran on the gravel of the Land's end, and Conor arrived at the old, old, very old man's house of the shining-white logs. With this old man, who rejoiced to see him safe returned, Conor spent the night, and on him bestowed the bottle of nectar that could never be emptied.

At Conor's request, the old man raised up from his stoney enchantment the half-brother, then gave them the bird to lead them to the house of the sky-blue logs. Another night they spent with the old, old man in the house of the sky-blue logs, and with him, who was delighted to see him back, Conor left the loaf of bread that could never be finished.

The old man raised from his enchantment the second half-brother and gave them the bounding copper ball, which led them to the house of the scarlet logs—where Conor and his half-brothers rested for the night. And with this old man, who was heartily rejoiced to see him safe, Conor left the ham that could never be cut out. And the old man raised up from enchantment the third of Conor's half-brothers.

Forward the four of them then went, traveling away and away, far farther than I could tell you, twice farther than you could tell me, and ten times farther than anyone else could tell the two of us, by hills and howes and thorny knowes, by green valley, moor, and mountain, by waving woods, shimmering lochs, and singing streams, by fairy raths and the Great Green Plain of Dreams. And at long last they reached Ireland.

When he came in sight of the King's Castle, Conor beheld the Queen still standing on the tower, a-watch for them. Immediately she saw Conor returning alive, she threw herself from the tower and was killed.

Great was the King his father's rejoicing at the coming of

Conor, whom he had long since given up for lost. He ordered that the most gorgeous feast ever given in Ireland should be prepared for a feast-day four weeks from this joyful day.

When the Queen of the Hill o' the World's End awoke, she told her ladies she had dreamt the loveliest dream of her life. She thought that a King's son, the handsomest of youths, came into the room while she slept and kissed her, and she had fallen in love with him.

"What a pity," said her ladies, "that it was only a dream."

She said, "I thought he took the ring from my finger, broke it, and tying one half on a silk ribbon around my neck, carried away the other half."

"But," said one of her ladies, "your ring is not on your finger. Half of it is hanging from a silk ribbon on your neck!"

Then the Queen, startled, found this was so and cried, "Was it dream or reality?" And she was lost in wonder.

When, soon they discovered the ham, loaf, and jug were gone, and water had been stolen from the Well o' the World's End, the Queen said, "The man who had the bravery to do this, which no other champion in the world before ever succeeded in doing, is surely the bravest and manliest of all men. Him, and only him, will I have for my King and husband. I'll set out and will never sleep two nights in the same bed, nor eat two meals' meat at the same table, till I have found the Noble One."

With her ladies nine, she set out, but found no trace of the youth she sought, till she reached the house of the shining white logs. There she saw her bottle of nectar; and the old man told her that the youth she was seeking was the King of Ireland's son, and had stayed there a night, and then gone forward to his brother in the house of the sky-blue logs.

At the house of the sky-blue logs she saw the loaf—and learned that Conor had stayed there a night and gone forward to the house of the scarlet logs. There she found the ham that could never be cut. And heard he had gone journeying for Ireland. And onward she pushed, with her companions, till she reached Ireland, and the King of Ireland's Castle.

The great feast in honor of Conor was about to begin when the King and the Court were summoned to behold, approaching, a wonderful cortege—a ravishingly beautiful maiden riding a white steed, with nine beautiful ladies on white steeds in her train. When she, the leader, reached the Castle's wondering crowd, she announced that she was the Queen of the Hill of the World's End, and that she came to seek and make her husband and King the Noble One who had been so brave as to reach and carry waters from the Well o' the World's End.

One after another, Conor's half-brothers arose, each claiming to be the gallant one. Of them the Queen asked, "Can you describe to me my castle and show me token of anything remarkable that you saw or did there?"

But neither the eldest nor the second nor the third half-brother, though he made the false claim, could describe or show token of a visit to her castle—and they had to sit down abashed.

Then the King cried, "Come you forward, my son, Conor!" And Conor modestly presented himself.

The Queen asked if it was he who had taken the bottles of water from the Well o' the World's End.

"It was I," said Conor.

"Did you take anything else?" asked the Queen.

Said Conor, "In your castle I beheld your beauty, as you slept, and couldn't refrain from taking a kiss."

From her neck she took the half-ring, asking him, "Can you match this?"

Conor produced the half-ring that exactly matched her piece.

When they saw that, all the Court and all the guests and the King, himself, cried out in rejoicement.

There and then brave Conor was married to the Beautiful Queen, and the great feast that was to have been Conor's, was the wedding feast of both. The feast lasted nine days and nine nights, and the last day and night were better than the first.

And Conor and his beautiful Queen lived happy and well ever after.